AT CAMP
KEE TOV

Ethics for Jewish Juniors

by **HELEN FINE**

Illustrated by **SEYMOUR FLEISHMAN**

UNION OF AMERICAN
HEBREW CONGREGATIONS
New York

AT CAMP
KEE TOV

Ethics for Jewish Juniors

To My
Beloved
Mother

Eighth Printing, 1979

Library of Congress
Catalogue Card Number: 61–0758

EDITOR'S INTRODUCTION

Ethical living takes the highest priority among the various forms of Jewish religious observance in the Reform interpretation of our tradition. Nothing therefore should receive more attention in our effort to instruct our children and adults in their religious responsibility. Yet the history of formal education in the area of ethics is beset by frustration and disappointment. It is reasonably easy to teach ethical phrases and slogans; it is not difficult to have children and even adults pronounce them with feeling and apparent commitment. Yet the correlation of behavior with ethical knowledge has neither been consistent nor reliable.

It is clear that instruction in ethics must not only reach the mind but go beyond it to the core of the individual's being. If the very self is not touched, if the ethical concern does not become part of one's very existence, the instruction will have been largely futile. Since such learning can best take place in actual situations, the classroom with its generally formal atmosphere may well be a questionable place for ethical instruction. It is only as the schoolroom deals with specific situations in the lives of children, made as realistic and as personally felt as it can be, that we have hope of teaching in the depth that we require. And it is only as the child sees the Jewish religious and intellectual roots of the ethical behavior which we are urging and for which he is reaching, that we achieve our unique purpose.

This volume is a pioneering effort to teach Jewish children

ethics in the context of their lives and in terms of the entire gamut of Jewish sources available to deal with them. Its accompanying Teacher's Book seeks to utilize the various modern techniques of pupil involvement on many levels to continue in a methodological way what has here been organized into the content of a course in ethics.

It is the hope of the Commission in sponsoring this volume that it may contribute to the more effective Jewish education of our children, and in this attempt we should be happy to be guided by the experience of parents and teachers using these materials.

RABBI EUGENE B. BOROWITZ
Director of Education

ACKNOWLEDGMENTS

In the Talmud the Rabbis say, "No matter how small the kindness, we should always feel gratefulness and express the feeling."

The many kindnesses extended to me have been far from small. In the tradition of the Talmud, it gives me joy to express my deep gratitude to all those who have helped me in the development of *At Camp Kee Tov.*

ESPECIALLY:

My rabbi, Roland B. Gittelsohn, for his continuing faith and encouragement.

The Reading Committee of the Commission on Jewish Education, Rabbi Leon Fram, Rabbi Samuel Glasner, Rabbi Abraham J. Klausner, Dr. Morton A. Seidenfeld, and Mrs. M.M. Singer, whose judicious criticisms and suggestions have helped to improve the manuscript immeasurably.

My principal, Mr. Samuel Nemzoff, under whose wise guidance I have experimented with the materials in this book.

The children in my religious school classes who have been eager participants in the preparation of this book.

Mr. Aaron Gordon, who shared his vast camping experiences with me when I sought his help.

Mrs. Julia Minor for her help in preparing the original manuscript.

Miss Sylvia Schiff who carefully proofread the manuscript, galleys, and pages.

Mr. Ralph Davis, who has created a skilfully designed book to capture the delight of children.

AND FINALLY:

My editor, Rabbi Eugene B. Borowitz, who inspired the book, guided its development, and whose brilliant insights I have attempted to interpret for pre-teen children.

MY GRATEFUL THANKS TO ALL OF YOU.

HELEN FINE

COMMISSION ON

JEWISH EDUCATION

of the UNION OF AMERICAN HEBREW CONGREGATIONS
and CENTRAL CONFERENCE OF AMERICAN RABBIS
AS OF 1961

ROLAND B. GITTELSOHN, *Chairman*
SOLOMON B. FREEHOF, *Honorary Chairman*
EUGENE B. BOROWITZ, *Director of Education*

BERNARD J. BAMBERGER	JAMES J. LEVBARG
DAVID I. CEDARBAUM	FELIX A. LEVY
MRS. HUGO DALSHEIMER	ALBERT M. LEWIS
LEON FRAM	JACOB R. MARCUS
ERIC FRIEDLAND	SAMUEL H. MARKOWITZ
SAMUEL GLASNER	MORTIMER MAY
NELSON GLUECK	EARL MORSE
EMANUEL GREEN	WALTER H. PLAUT
JOSEPH HARLAM	DAVID RIFF
JAMES G. HELLER	JACOB P. RUDIN
ABRAHAM J. KLAUSNER	LAWRENCE W. SCHWARTZ
TOBY K. KURZBAND	SYLVAN D. SCHWARTZMAN
MEIR LASKER	MRS. M. M. SINGER
SIDNEY M. LEFKOWITZ	PAUL M. STEINBERG
ARTHUR J. LELYVELD	J. JACQUES STONE

EMANUEL GAMORAN, *Honorary Member*
MAURICE N. EISENDRATH, *Secretary*

UNION GRADED SERIES

EDITED BY

RABBI EUGENE B. BOROWITZ, *Director of Education*
UNION OF AMERICAN HEBREW CONGREGATIONS

CONTENTS

ix

AT CAMP
KEE TOV
Ethics for Jewish Juniors

1. PLEASED TO MEET YOU!

"There it is! There it is!" cried Marsha, pointing to a huge sign. "See! Our camp!"

Daddy turned the car into a road on the right.

"I hope the campers choose Kee Tov for the new name this summer, don't you, Michael?" Marsha looked at her twin brother, hopefully.

"I sure do!" agreed Michael.

A warning look appeared on Mother's face. "Now Twins," she said, "if Kee Tov isn't chosen, I hope you won't be too disappointed. It depends on the vote."

Marsha gave her mother a hug. "Don't worry, Mother. We know that. But we can wish—can't we?"

Choosing a name for the camp had been a Ross family project. A week ago they had gathered in the back garden. "Let's choose the name for camp now," Marsha said, "we have to send it to Aaron Green tomorrow." Daddy sent Michael into the house for Aaron's letter. When he came back Daddy read the letter to the family.

3

Union-Institute
The Camp for Living Judaism
Sinai, New Hampshire

Dear Marsha and Michael:

At the beginning of each season it is our custom to give a Hebrew name to our camp. You, the campers, choose it. The Hebrew name you choose must come from the Bible. It must express what you want this camp to mean to you. Please send your choice to me one week before camp opens. The staff will help me to select the seven best names. On the first night at camp you will vote for the name you like best.

Sincerely,
AARON GREEN, *Director*

When he finished reading, Daddy looked up. "Any ideas, Twins?" Michael was the first to speak. "I think our name should have something to do with God."

"Why do you say that?" asked Mother.

"Well," replied Michael, "God made the world and God made us—and God is still doing things. He never stops for a second."

Daddy was pleased with Michael's explanation. "That's right, I guess that's what we mean when we say He is a *living* God. What would you say was God's first act?"

Michael's answer came quickly. "God created the world the very first thing."

"Good," Daddy said, "then perhaps our name for the camp can be found at the beginning of the Book of Genesis. Let's get the Bible and read the first chapter together."

When Michael brought the Bible everyone listened carefully as Daddy read. " 'In the beginning God created the heaven and earth.' " When he finished the chapter Daddy closed the Bible and looked at his family. "Well," he asked with a smile, "any ideas now?"

Marsha's face lit up. "After God created each thing in the world," she said, "the Bible tells us that He looked at it and saw that it was good. What does that mean, Daddy?"

"In simple words it means 'God was pleased with the good world He made,' " Daddy answered.

"If God saw that the world was good," continued Marsha, "and the Bible keeps saying that over and over again, couldn't we get a Hebrew name from those words? Couldn't we?"

Michael groaned. "What kind of name is that? 'Camp and God Saw That It Was Good!' By the time we rolled that out of our mouths, we'd be late for dinner."

"Just a minute," interrupted Mother, looking at Daddy, "what are the Hebrew words for 'And God saw that it was good'?"

Opening the Bible, Daddy ran his finger along the page until he matched the Hebrew words with the English translation. "*Va-yar Elohim Kee Tov*," he read.

"Kee Tov," shouted the twins together.

"Kee Tov," echoed their parents.

They rolled the words around on their tongues again and again. Yes, they liked Kee Tov very much—it was just right.

"It sounds good," said Marsha, with a chuckle, "and it means good." She twinkled up at her brother. "And it is a good world—aren't we going to a dandy camp?"

At that minute Michael remembered that the world wasn't always good. That morning he had broken Daddy's electric drill and hidden the pieces. It had taken him a long time to admit the truth. Now he had to miss the Boy Scout picnic and clean the cellar instead. He gazed at his family with a serious expression on his face. "It's not always a good world," he announced sadly, "sometimes it's a bad one."

Marsha looked with surprise at her twin. "When it's a bad world it's not God's fault. It's ours."

Daddy and Mother nodded in agreement. "Most of the time that's true," said Daddy, "God made a good world, and if we do the right things we can make it better."

"One way is to face up to our mistakes," said Michael. "I hope I remember that."

"Kee Tov," said Daddy and Mother again.

And now they had finally arrived at camp.

They drove along the road until they came to a huge house built of soft-colored gray rock. A porch crowded with people stretched along the front. Surrounding the house were wide lawns dotted with oak trees.

In the great hall of the Big House they waited in line to see Aaron, the director. When their turn came, he greeted them with a warm handshake. "Now, let me see," he said, studying a chart. "Michael, you're in bunk six, and Marsha, you're in bunk six, too. But," Aaron added with a smile, "your bunks are in different places."

Then he turned to Mother and Daddy. "You can take them over to their bunks now. Their trunks have arrived and their counselors are waiting to greet them." Nodding, the director then went on to welcome the next family in line.

Mother took Marsha's hand. "Come, Marsha," she said, "let's get you settled." They followed a path leading to the Girls' Village.

"Here's bunk six, Mother," said Marsha, stopping suddenly. She tightened her hold on Mother's hand. All at once the thought of facing a group of strangers made her afraid. "What if the girls don't like me?" she asked, looking anxiously up at her mother.

Mother laughed. "Of course, they'll like you, darling. If all of you make up your minds to help each other, you'll be happy. I don't see how you can miss having a wonderful summer." Mother squeezed Marsha's hand to give her courage. Marsha felt better right away.

When Marsha and her mother opened the screen door, the excited voices inside rushed at them like a jet stream. A tall, dark, gray-eyed girl separated herself from the noise and came to greet them. She introduced herself as Miriam Levitt, Marsha's counselor. Marsha's blue eyes lit up with pleasure as soon as she shook hands. Miriam turned to the girls, who had stopped chat-

tering to look at Marsha. "Come on, gang! Introduce your-selves to Marsha Ross."

"Hi, Marsha! Glad to have you aboard. I'm Susan Berensen. I'm a twin, too. But my brother is at another camp. We fight too much."

"Hi, too. I'm Ann Glick. Everyone calls me 'Freckles.'" Ann pointed to her face with a scowl. "I'm sure you can see why," she added.

Marsha waited for the last girl to introduce herself but the girl didn't say a word. After a long second Marsha held out her hand. The girl took the hand and gave Marsha a shy smile. Miriam decided to step in at this point. "This is Tamar Slezac. Tamar comes from Hungary. She's been in America for two years now."

Tamar gazed at Marsha and found her tongue. "I am pleased to make your acquaintance." Her voice was soft and the way she spoke English sounded strange to Marsha's ears.

"Our fifth bunkmate hasn't arrived yet," said Miriam. "Her name is Sara Miller and she comes from New York."

While the girls were unpacking, Miriam walked with Mother to the small porch in front of the cabin. "I've heard that Marsha has an unusual imagination."

Mother beamed. "Thank you, Miriam. Marsha's never been away from home before. I hope she'll get along with every-body."

Miriam laughed and nodded toward the cabin. "That chatter inside sounds as if they're off to a good start already."

Mother called to Marsha but she was too busy to listen. "I can see what you mean," Mother chuckled, "tell Marsha to meet her father and me at the Big House in an hour to say good-bye. If anything comes up, please get in touch with me. And have a pleasant summer, Miriam."

Miriam went inside and Mother started to walk toward the Big House. Suddenly she stopped. Coming toward her were a man and woman dragging a sobbing girl between them. "I won't stay! I won't stay!" cried the girl, struggling to get away from their grasp. "I don't want you to go to Europe and leave me alone! Please, Daddy? Please, Mother? I'll die if I stay here!" She was crying as if her heart would break.

"Goodness—that must be Sara Miller," thought Mother, "I hope she won't upset the girls."

Drawn by the noise of the crying, Miriam and the girls ran out to the porch, their eyes bright with curiosity. Miriam looked at Sara and came to a quick decision. "Girls, why don't you finish unpacking?" She waited for them to return to the cabin before she spoke.

"Hello, Sara," said Miriam kindly, "welcome to camp."

Sara stamped her foot at Miriam.

"I won't stay! I won't stay in this crummy old camp!" she cried. Sara's sobs were louder now and her eyes flashed fire at everyone. No one was going to make her do what she didn't want to do! She'd show them!

Sara's parents couldn't meet Miriam's eyes. "Now, look here, Sara," said her mother, "when we come back we'll bring you some lovely gifts. Daddy and I must go to Europe on business. Stop being such a baby and behave yourself." Mrs. Miller's voice grew louder. "I'm ashamed of you and in front of all these people, too. What will they think of you?"

"I don't want your old presents and I don't care what people think!" Sara's angry words hit her parents like a whiplash.

Miriam grasped Sara's hand firmly. "Let's go inside and meet the other girls. Say good-bye to your parents, Sara."

When her parents bent toward her to kiss her, Sara twisted away from them. She knew she had to stay at camp but she'd find a way to get even. She'd fix them!

"All right! I'll stay, but I won't be good! You'll see!" She glared at Miriam through wet eyes and added, "You're not going to like me, you know."

Miriam smiled. "I'm going to try hard to change your mind,

Sara." She started back to the cabin. Sara walked stiffly beside her without a backward glance at her unhappy parents.

Mr. and Mrs. Miller watched their daughter disappear into the cabin and joined Mrs. Ross. Mrs. Miller sighed. "I don't know what gets into her. I admit she's spoiled. She's our only child. But that scene! What a bad first impression she's making!"

Mrs. Ross tried to comfort Sara's mother even though she was worried herself. How would Marsha and the other girls feel about Sara? Would Sara bring trouble to the bunk? "I liked the way Miriam handled Sara. Didn't you? So patient, yet so firm."

"It's about time my daughter began to realize she's not the only one in the world," said Mr. Miller, gruffly. "Those tantrums are getting pretty tough to take."

Meanwhile Michael and his father walked down the road to the Boys' Village. They stopped to admire a huge outdoor theater that was surrounded by poplar trees.

As they caught sight of the cabins, Michael looked at his father and asked, "Dad, do you think the boys will like me?"

Daddy smiled at the worried look on Michael's face. "That depends on you. The way I see it, you've got to listen to the other fellow's side and try to put yourself in his place. And if things go wrong, face up to it. The electric drill, remember?"

"Thanks, Dad," said Michael, remembering very well. "You always know the right thing to say to a fellow."

Outside bunk six they saw Michael's counselor sitting on the grass. Four boys were buzzing him with questions.

"Will we go on an overnight hike?"

"Can I go swimming today?"

"When are we going to play baseball?"

"When do we eat?"

Michael walked over to the group. "Hi kids! I'm Michael Ross. Boy, am I glad to be here!"

The counselor rose to his feet with a big grin. "I'm Bill Sherman, the about-to-be-counselor of this noisy gang," he laughed, shaking hands with Michael and his father. "Welcome to our bunk, Michael." He turned to the boys.

"Introductions are now in order." The boys stood at attention like soldiers ready for inspection.

"Jeffrey Golden," said a boy with curly hair, "super spaceman of bunk six."

"That's why his hair is so curly," laughed Bill, "it curls up in fright at some of his orbiting ideas."

Jeffrey's merry gray eyes smiled at Michael. "How would you like to take a ride to the moon with me?" Jeff pretended to blast off, brushing his palms together toward the sky.

"Will do!" giggled Michael, liking Jeffrey right away.

"Steven Rome." A tall boy stepped up in front of Michael. "Hey, are you a good baseball player? We need a good team to win the championship."

Baseball! Michael swallowed hard. Baseball wasn't his game! No matter how hard he tried, he missed the pitch or the catch. "Not a very good one," he admitted, wishing he could play better.

Steven frowned. "Gosh, I was hoping our whole bunk would be good. I hit more home runs in the Little League this year than anyone on my team. Maybe I can give you some pointers."

"Thanks," said Michael, hoping the other boys didn't share Steven's feelings. It was easy to see that Steven was wild about the game. Michael looked at his father who had been helping him with his game all spring. Mr. Ross looked back at his son, understanding just how he felt.

"I'm Ben Arkin." Michael saw a boy as round as a barrel holding a small camera. He pointed it at Michael and pretended to take his picture. "Cameras and food are my favorite hobbies."

Bill himself introduced the last boy to Michael. "This is Joshua Keller."

Michael looked into two warm brown eyes. Suddenly, he noticed the white cane in Joshua's hand. "Why, he's blind!"

thought Michael, gazing at the cane. He stared first at his father, then at Bill, and finally at the boys. An uncomfortable silence spread through the group.

Joshua broke the quiet. Pointing the cane at Michael, he said with a friendly grin, "And this is my trusty cane. It sticks to me like glue. Where I go, my cane goes." The words tumbled out of Joshua's mouth and his eyes darted eagerly around the circle. Michael found his tongue. "Hello, Joshua," he said. Grabbing the end of the cane, Michael gave it a hearty shake. "Hello Joshua's cane," he chuckled.

Bill interrupted the conversation. "Come on gang! Last one into the bunk is a sputnik!" Into the cabin they scrambled with a whoop. Bill and Mr. Ross could hear the boys calling Ben the sputnik.

"I should have told Michael about Joshua," said Mr. Ross to Bill, "Aaron Green wrote to me about him. Michael's never met a blind person before. His silence must have been embarrassing to Joshua. It's my fault."

"Not at all, Mr. Ross. Josh and I have been here all week learning how to get about the camp. He is an amazing boy. The courage with which he accepts his blindness is a wonderful thing to see."

Shortly afterwards the twins joined their parents.

Mother looked anxiously at them. "Now, be careful when you go into the water. Be sure to obey the rules."

"We will, Mother!"

Daddy warned, "Be sure to wear your rubbers and raincoats when it rains."

"We will, Daddy!"

Mother added, "Be sure to eat everything."

"We will, Mother!"

The twins looked at each other and giggled.

"We will!" they said together.

Daddy was puzzled. "What was that for? We didn't say anything!"

Michael grinned. "You'll think of something else. You always do!"

Daddy and Mother gave them each a spank, then climbed into the car.

"Now remember, Twins," said Daddy, "we're not around to help you obey the rules. You're on your own and you have to think for yourselves. Mother and I won't be here to tell you what is right or wrong. You'll have to decide for yourselves. Will you try to remember that?"

"See, Dad," laughed Michael, "I said you'd think of something else."

"We're very serious about this, Michael," said Mother. "That's why we sent you here."

The twins promised to remember.

The last thing Mother and Daddy saw as their car rolled away was Michael and Marsha jumping up and down in the middle of the road waving wildly.

WHAT DO YOU THINK?

1. The Bible tells us that Job thought he didn't deserve the suffering that came into his life. He complained to God about his troubles. Three friends who came to visit Job were shocked to hear Job talk this way. Yet, the Bible tells us that God listened to Job and not to his friends.

   The Rabbis in the Talmud said that this story teaches us, "A person should not be held completely responsible for what he does when he is suffering."

   Inside the girls' cabin, Sara flung herself on her bunk and refused to speak to anyone. When the girls tried to be friendly she was rude. Miriam said to the girls, "Sara's too upset and unhappy now. She isn't thinking clearly. Let's leave her alone until she feels better."

How was Sara like Job in the Bible?

What did Miriam say to the girls about Sara that reminds you of the advice in the Talmud?

What would you have said to Sara if you had been in the cabin and she was rude to you?

2. Our Rabbis also taught, "A person should always be patient like Hillel."

Do you remember any of the stories about Hillel's patience? (Hint: the most famous one is about a man who wanted to learn the whole Torah while he stood on one foot.)

How was Miriam's patience with Sara like Hillel's?

3. The Talmud says, "What you say about yourself is not as good an advertisement as what others say about you."

When Steven bragged to Michael about his baseball score, how did it make you feel?

Have you ever wished with all your heart that you could be a better athlete? What advice could you give Michael that might help him to improve his game?

4. The Fifth Commandment in the Bible says, "Honor your father and mother."

How was Sara breaking God's commandment? Was it Sara's fault?

How were the twins obeying this commandment?

What makes the commandment hard to obey? How can we obey it more often?

5. "God advises us; but the choice of doing right or wrong rests with ourselves."

How will this Talmud saying help the twins at camp?

How can it help you?

When you do something wrong, how do you feel?

Why did Daddy give this advice to the twins before he left them?

6. In the Bible God says, "You shall not take revenge or bear a grudge against the children of your people."

   What did Sara say that tells us she had forgotten this law?

   Do you think Sara will be happier when she tries to seek revenge?

   Whom will she harm the most? In what way?

7. *Do you think Sara's parents were too easy with her? Too hard?*

   What would you have said to Sara if you had been Miriam? Her mother?

   Her father? Mrs. Ross?

   Let's dramatize the different conversations.

8. When they were studying about the Creation in religious school, Marsha and Michael heard this story:
   The Rabbis in the Talmud wrote that God said, "Of what use are all the good things I have created unless men are there to enjoy them?"

   How does this Talmud statement show that the Rabbis felt God loves us?

   Does God expect us to be good all the time?

   How did Michael decide to try to help God keep His world good?

   Do you like the reason why the twins chose Kee Tov as the new camp name? Why?

9. The Midrash tells us that some Rabbis imagined that God created other worlds before He created this one. But they were not satisfactory ones so He destroyed them. Finally, God created a world that was good for men to dwell in. To show that God really wanted this kind of world, the Bible tells us

that after each thing was created, "God saw that it was good." When the world was finished God saw that it was very good for men to live in.

How does this story show that Jews believe God loves us?

2. THE TREE OF LIFE

Aaron rapped for attention and waited for the dining hall to be quiet. "The most important thing we have to decide tonight is the special name for our camp this summer. The staff and I have chosen seven Hebrew names. We feel they best express what we hope this camp will mean to you. Later on we are going to ask you to vote for the one you like the best. The children whose names I read, please meet me on the porch of the Big House after our closing prayer."

Michael heard Aaron say, "Ross Twins." He searched the hall for Marsha. When he caught her eye they smiled happily at each other.

Aaron began the closing prayer. "And now let us thank God for providing us and all living creatures with the food we have eaten."

"*Boruch ato Adonoi ha-zon es ha-kol,*" sang the campers. And in English they said, "Praised be Thou, O Lord, who provides food for all."

Excusing himself, Michael hurried to meet Marsha outside the hall.

17

Walking toward the Big House they told each other about their bunkmates with excited voices.

Marsha chattered like a magpie. "I just love Miriam—I love her zillions! She's a religious school teacher and she teaches the fourth grade in public school, too. Tamar comes from Hungary —she's shy. And Michael, her English has the funniest sound! And Ann—she has the biggest freckles you ever saw—and Susan is so funny. Her jokes make all of us laugh. The only one in our bunk who isn't friendly is Sara. Miriam says that she's unhappy and we have to help her." As Marsha stopped for breath, Michael saw his chance to get a few words into the conversation.

"We have a blind boy in our bunk!"

"A blind boy!" Marsha looked at her brother unbelievingly.

"Wait till you meet him! You won't even be able to tell. Joshua—that's his name—told me he had to learn to walk with his eyes closed. He has to depend on his memory for everything."

"How does he keep from bumping into everything?"

"He was here at camp all last week and Bill—he's our counselor—brailled the camp for him and he brailled the bunk, too."

"Brailled! What's that?" Marsha's eyes grew rounder and rounder.

"Joshua uses the face of a clock to tell directions. He's always the center of the clock. When he stands in the middle of the bunk facing the washroom he knows my bed next to his is at three o'clock. His bed next to mine is at four o'clock. Bill's bed across the room is at eight o'clock and the washroom is at twelve o'clock. He eats like that, too. Bill and Joshua are going to teach us all about Joshua's clock routine so we can help him when he wants to see anything."

"See! How can a blind person see?"

"He can see with his mind, with his hands, and with all his other senses except his eyes."

"How will he get around the camp?"

"He has a white cane. All the boys will have to be sure that nothing in the bunk is changed without telling Joshua about it. Doors have to be shut or open all the way so that he won't bump and hurt himself. Bill says we'll have to think about it all the time so we'll get into the habit of keeping Joshua safe."

Marsha had one more question. "Does Joshua mind when Bill tells you how to help him?"

"Of course not, silly," Michael shook his head impatiently at his sister. "He just laughs and jokes about it. He says that it took a long time for him to learn, too. Besides, he wanted to come to camp because he was so lonely. And Marsha—he plays the violin. He's going to play for the choir when they sing for the Sabbath services."

Marsha looked up to see Aaron motioning for them to hurry. When they walked up on the porch, Aaron introduced them to the other children.

"Let's get down to business," announced Aaron, smiling at the circle around him. "Each of you quoted a sentence from the Bible and took one or more of the Hebrew words in the sentence to be used as a name of the camp. I am going to ask each of you to recite your sentences to the campers. Then in a few words tell why you chose your name. Is that clear?"

Michael's heart slipped down to his sneakers. The idea of standing in front of everybody at camp frightened him. Glancing at Marsha he saw her lower lip quiver and knew she felt the same way.

Aaron saw the scared looks. "Now, Twins, wait a minute. There's nothing to get panicky about. You've been in plays before. This is just like a play and you are the actors. Now—is that hard to do?"

The memory of their Purim play at religious school and the fun they had had gave the twins back some of their courage.

"Sit over there on the side porch," said Aaron, "and plan

what you want to say. I. know you can do it." Aaron made the twins feel as brave as a barrel of lions. They practiced what they wanted to say until they were letter perfect.

At seven o'clock the camp gathered in the open air theater. The camp was divided into three sections. The *Giborim*, the oldest children in camp, sat at the right of the stage. The *Na-arim*, the next oldest, sat at the left. In the center were the *Y'lodim*, the youngest campers.

Aaron began the program. "The children on this stage reached into the Torah—the Bible—to find a name for our camp. Now—why do you suppose I asked you to look in the Torah? Because its wise words tell us how to live with ourselves and how to live with each other. If we know and understand its laws we can learn the difference between right and wrong. Our Torah helps us to know what God wants us to do."

Aaron looked out at the audience and paused for a minute. "When you have decided on the name you want, check it on the ballot, and pass it to your counselors." Aaron signaled for the first boy on the stage to come forward.

"My quotation comes from Genesis 1:27," he began. " 'And God created man in His own image.' When God made us He gave us the precious gift of life. If we obey His commandments we will grow to be more like God. My choice is *B'tzalmo* which is the Hebrew for 'in His image.' "

The second boy walked to the front of the stage. "My name comes from Psalm 11:7, 'For the Lord is righteous, He loveth righteousness.' We grow to know God by doing kind acts. My name is *Tzedek* which means 'righteousness.' "

The third speaker was a girl. "My choice is found in Leviticus 19:18, 'Thou shalt love thy neighbor as thyself.' We show our love for God in the way we love each other. We must put ourselves in the same place as our neighbor and then act toward him as we would act towards ourselves. My name is *Ohavto* which means 'you shall love.' "

Next came one of the older girls. "My quotation comes from

Psalm 15:1, 2, 'Who shall dwell upon Thy holy mountain? He that walketh uprightly, and worketh righteousness, and speaketh truth in his heart.' We must not only speak the truth—we must also think the truth. Our words and our thoughts must match. My name is *Emes B'libo* which means 'truth in his heart.' "

Another older girl came forward. "My choice comes from Ecclesiastes 7:20, 'For there is not a righteous man upon earth, that doeth good and sinneth not.' No matter how good we are, we all make mistakes. But God loves us even when we make mistakes if we are truly sorry and try to do better. My name is *Ya-aseh Tov* which means 'he does good.' "

The sixth speaker said, "My quotation comes from Exodus 19:5, 'Ye shall be Mine own treasure from among all peoples.' The Jews were not chosen by God to receive the Torah until they promised to obey all its commandments. My name is *S'goolo* which means 'treasure.' "

At last came the twins' turn. Their hearts pounded like hammers.

"Our quotation comes from Genesis, too—1:31, 'And God saw everything that He had made, and behold, it was very good.' God created the world little by little. He was pleased with His work. God is good and the world He created for us is good."

Michael continued, "It is up to us to keep the world God created a good world and to keep making it better. If we follow God's commandments wherever we are, we help to make His world good. Our Hebrew name is *Kee Tov* which means—'that it was good.' "

The audience clapped long and hard until Aaron raised his hands. "While we're waiting for the votes to be counted, let's hear from some of the people who are going to help you have a good time this summer." Aaron called to a man standing nearby. "Roy, will you say a few words of welcome?" Roy jumped up on the stage.

"Hi, gang! I'm your head counselor. Those were good ideas we just heard, weren't they? If all of us follow them there won't be any problems in camp, will there? Just one thing more. If you have anything bothering you and you think I can help—don't hesitate to come to me. I don't promise to do what you want me to do—but I'll listen with nine ears."

The Giborim were ready with a cheer for Roy:

SNICKETY, SNACKITY, SNOCKITY, SNOO,
ROY WILL BE WILLING TO LISTEN TO YOU!

"Dorothy, our head counselor in the Girls' Village," said Aaron, "has a word for you, too." Dorothy walked up the stairs.

"Welcome to camp, all of you out there! A warm smile, a friendly hello, a kind deed, a shared adventure—all of these spell happiness for you and for your friends. If you can remember this—then you are on the right road."

The Na-arim were ready with another cheer:

RICKETY, RACKITY, ROCKITY, ROO.
DOROTHY'S ADVICE IS THE BEST FOR YOU.

Aaron signaled to a man in the back. "Everyone knows that one of the signs of a happy camp is good food." Aaron's mustache curled up into a smile when a cheer swept through the room. "Joe has been with us for a thousand years. He knows what children like to eat and he knows how to cook it, too. Come on up, Joe, and tell them all about it."

A roly-poly, bald-headed man leaped on the stage. Joe stood there laughing so hard his fat stomach shivered like a bowl of jello.

"Well, kids," boomed Joe, "you won't go hungry, that I guarantee. You all know that a fat cook is a good sign. It means he enjoys his own cooking. And I am a fat cook!" Joe winked at the campers and threw his head back with a roar.

The Y'lodim were ready with a cheer for Joe:

TICKETY, TOCKETY, TACKETY, TOE—
JOE IS THE ONE WHO IS BEST TO KNOW!

"And now here's Mary, our camp nurse," Aaron said with a smile, as Mary tripped up to the stage. Mary's hair was like spun gold and her eyes were as blue as the sea. When she spoke she warmed the campers right down to their toes. "I'm the one who iodines you—pills you—vitamins you—bandages you—and temperatures you. I want to remind you of one thing, though: there's a new fire law this season—at no time are there to be more than 27 children in the infirmary at one time. So-o-o-o-o-o-o, please try not to rush at me all at once." Mary finished with an old-fashioned curtsy. The children whistled and stamped. This time everyone joined in for the cheer:

GREEN PILLS, PINK PILLS,
ANY STYLE.
MARY GIVES THEM
WITH A SMILE!

Aaron continued.

"Our camp rabbi, Bill Sherman, is helping to count the votes." Aaron pointed to Bill at the back of the theater, "Next year our Bill will become a full-fledged rabbi when he graduates from the Hebrew Union College-Jewish Institute of Religion in Cincinnati. Bill is a famous story teller. He can tell a story at the drop of a hat—anywhere—anytime! He'll make the people in the Torah and the Talmud and the Midrash come alive before your very eyes."

"That's *my* counselor," said Michael, beaming at Marsha. He glanced out at his bunkmates and chuckled when he saw their thumbs stuck in their armpits, grinning at each other.

Aaron went down the stairs to help an old man with snowy

hair up to the stage. "One of the most popular members of our camp family is our caretaker, Mr. Jacob Levy—Gramps, to you. Gramps has been with us ever since this camp opened. For most of his life, Gramps has been studying the Torah which makes him just about the wisest man at camp."

Gramps interrupted Aaron with a fond glance. "I'm afraid Aaron is exaggerating, children. You can never really know *all* the Torah. I'm still learning something new each day."

Aaron smiled at Gramps. "Now remember this," he said to the campers, "if you really want some good advice any time this summer, Gramps is the one to ask. He's never too busy to listen. And—" Aaron twinkled at the children, "he always sweetens his advice with something good to eat—something that you're sure to like."

At that moment Bill came running down the aisle holding a paper in the air. The vote was counted! Sitting on the edges of their benches the campers waited breathlessly. Who would be the winner?

For a long minute Aaron looked at the paper. He cleared his throat once and cleared it again. "The winning name is—" Aaron studied the paper once more. The campers groaned. "The name *you* have chosen is—KEE TOV! Marsha and Michael Ross—come forward and take a well-earned bow!"

The campers stamped and they whistled and they shouted.

It didn't take long for the Giborim to make up a cheer for Michael and Marsha.

TASSITY, TESSITY, TOSS
MARSHA AND MICHAEL ROSS.
KEE TOV! RAH! RAH! RAH!
KEE TOV! BIM! BOOM! BAH!

The twins listened to the cheer with flushed surprised faces. Marsha whispered to Michael, "I didn't dream that Kee Tov would win. The other names were so wonderful!"

"Me neither! I thought Emes B'libo was the best."

Gramps smiled at the twins and put his arms around their shoulders.

"Hold it a minute!" came a loud voice from the audience, "I want to take that picture!" The twins looked out and saw Ben standing on a bench aiming his camera at them. They all grinned when Ben clicked the camera.

Gramps had something more to say. "The Torah has passed down to us through many generations. What I have seen and heard here tonight makes me sure that it is safe in your hands." Gramps' face shone as if a lighted candle were held to it. " 'The Torah is a tree of life—*ets chayim*—to them who hold fast to it.' The roots are our belief in God. The trunk is the way we grow to know God. The branches are the protection that God gives us. The fruit is the lovingkindness, the truth, the justice, and the peace that we feel each day when we live our lives in the right way. And the flowers stand for the heart which finds joy in serving God."

Gramps hugged the twins to him. "Kee Tov is a good name for our camp. It says, 'Thank you, God, for creating a good world for us.' And it holds you to a promise—a promise to God to try to share this good world with each other."

WHAT DO YOU THINK?

1. The Bible says, "Thou shalt love thy neighbor as thyself."

   How will Joshua's bunkmates help to carry out this commandment?

   If you were Joshua how would you feel when you discovered how willing the boys were to help you?

   Put yourself in Joshua's place and say the words that you feel in your heart.

2. The Talmud says, "You were surprised but I was more surprised."

   What did the twins say to each other that reminds you of this quotation?

   Have you ever won a contest? Were you surprised?

   Did you think you should have won it? Why? Why not?

3. *What do you think of the way the campers chose a name for the camp?*

   How does it remind you of our American way of life?

   Which name would you have chosen? Why?

4. Later that evening Gramps suggested to Aaron that the bunks be given Hebrew names instead of numbers. Gramps thought the other Hebrew names submitted by the campers would make wonderful names for the bunks.

   Which name would you have chosen for your bunk? Why?

   Can you think of any other names that could be used?

   Look in the Bible for ideas.

5. *Which person that Aaron introduced to the campers did you like the best?*

   Which person made you feel as if you could go to him for help if you needed help? Why do we feel we can talk to some people easier than to others?

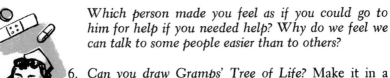

6. *Can you draw Gramps' Tree of Life? Make it in a scroll like a Torah and add the rollers. Then label the parts according to Gramps' description.*

7. The Bible says, "And the man Moses was very meek above all the men who were on the face of the earth."

   Did Gramps say anything in the story that makes you feel he is like Moses?

8. Find two places in the story where the children thanked God for the good things He provides for us.

Why do you think Gramps felt that Kee Tov said, "Thank you, God"?

How does the lovingkindness we show to the people around us show that we are thanking God for His care?

3. A DISAPPOINTMENT FOR STEVEN

In bunk six that night the boys were preparing for bed. Joshua was ready first. Bill was everywhere checking to be sure the boys had washed all over and brushed their teeth. Ben was putting new film in his camera. He hadn't done anything but get into his pajamas.

"Come on Ben, you're holding up the works!" said Bill.

"Who, me? I'm in my pajamas! I've been ready for a century and a half!" Ben grinned at Bill and shut his camera with a click.

Bill took hold of Ben's ear. "March!" he ordered, pointing to the washroom with a steely finger.

"But soap isn't good for my face. My skin's too sensitive!" Ben wriggled out of Bill's grasp, laughing up at him.

"Will you wash up or do I do it for you?" asked Bill, pretending to roll up his sleeves.

"O.K., O.K. Everywhere I go people are telling me to wash!" The boys could hear him grumbling as he opened the water tap. All at once they heard a scream. Ben came flying out holding a bar of soap. "Hey! Look! A spider climbed up on my soap!" All of the boys rushed to circle Ben and to look at the spider.

Bill laughed and picked up the spider. Walking to the open door he tossed it out into the air. He turned around to see David throwing his pillow at Steven. Steven ducked to the floor and the pillow plopped onto Jeff. "I've been hit by a rocket gun!" shouted Jeff, tackling David's leg.

Bill separated the laughing heap. "Quit the clowning," he said, "I've got important things to discuss with you." Just then Ben appeared. His face was so scrubbed that each freckle shone separately. "Satisfied?" Ben asked, cocking his head at Bill.

"Not bad!" Bill ran his finger along the water mark on Ben's neck.

"Lucky you're not a giraffe. Now *he* has a neck to wash!"

"Bill," asked Joshua, "do you think Gramps looks a little like Moses in the Bible?" An explosion of laughter greeted his question.

"Moses had a beard," said Ben. "At least he has one in all the pictures I've seen. Gramps hasn't a beard, Josh."

"Wait a minute, fellows," said Bill, "I think I know what Josh means. And I agree. Gramps *is* like Moses. He loves people as Moses did and he cares for his plants in the chapel just as tenderly as Moses cared for his flocks in the desert. The Rabbis in the Midrash told us how Moses watched over the flocks of Jethro, his father-in-law. One day, while Moses was tending his flock, a little kid escaped and ran away. Moses followed it to a nearby stream and watched it drink its fill of cool water. 'Poor little goat,' said Moses, 'I didn't know that your thirst made you run away. How tired you must be!' Moses lifted the kid onto his shoulders and carried it back to the flock. God saw how kind Moses was. Then He knew Moses would be a good leader for His people. God didn't give Moses the job of leading His people out of Egyptian slavery until He had tested him in small things."

Bill smiled at the eager listening faces and continued. "God

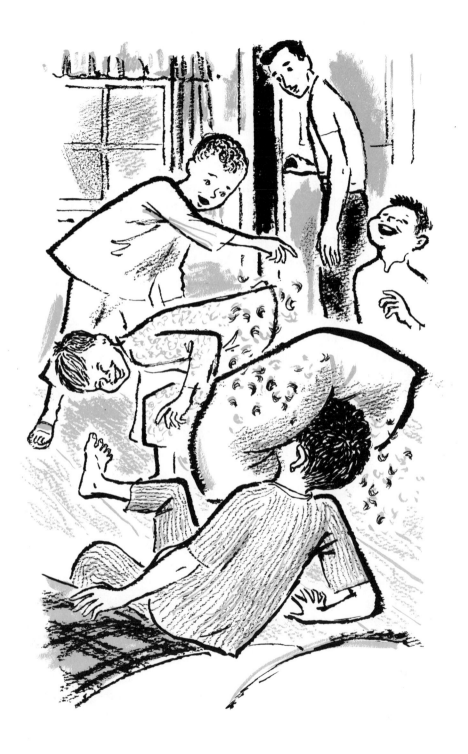

said, 'He who understands how to pasture a flock, providing for each what is good for it, he shall pasture My people.' "

"But Gramps isn't a leader," objected Steven. "A leader has to be a president or a captain of a baseball team or something like that!"

"That's where you're wrong, Steven," said Bill. "Gramps *is* a leader! Right here at camp he'll prove that to you. The way he listens to you makes you want to listen to him. When you go to the Thinking Place you'll discover that!"

"Thinking Place! What in the world is that?" asked Michael.

"It's the pine grove leading from Universal Lawn behind the Big House. When a camper has a problem he goes there to think about it. Most of the time you'll find Gramps there. When he isn't caring for his plants in the chapel he goes there to study the Torah."

"Study!" interrupted Jeff, "why should Gramps still be studying? He's so old!"

Bill shook his head. "No one knows all he has to know about God and about doing good. No one's too old to study the Torah. You heard Gramps tell you that he is still learning things from the Torah and he's been studying all his life. Yes, I agree with Josh. Gramps *is* like Moses. And now—" said Bill, changing the subject, "one of the things we have to decide tonight is the delegate you want this bunk to send to camp council."

Bill could see the questions in the boys' eyes. He lifted his hands. "Hold the questions for a minute and let me explain. The delegates you choose will elect one of the Giborim to be president. Together, with the help of the staff, the council runs the camp. They draw up a list of duties and you choose the job you feel you can do best. Of course, you might not get to do the work you want to do the first week, but by the end of the summer you'll have had a try at everything."

"What are some of the duties, Bill?" asked Joshua, wondering what he could do.

·"Well, there's kitchen duty—setting the tables, folding napkins, washing silverware—"

"That's for me," said Ben, winking at Bill, "where the kitchen is, I am!"

Bill ignored Ben's wisecrack and continued. "Some of you will be on the cleaning squads—keeping the camp grounds and the beach clean. Some of you will mow the lawn and sweep the buildings. If everyone pitches in, the work gets done quickly and the camp runs smoothly."

"I can fold napkins and wipe silverware," said Joshua, relieved to discover something he could do.

"Another duty of the camp council," continued Bill, "is to act on the campers' suggestions that make our camp better. If you think of any good ideas, the council will try to put them into action. In that way, we share our ideas as well as our duties."

"That reminds me of the family councils we have at home," remembered Michael. He looked around at the boys. They had turned out to be a dandy bunch of kids. He gazed at Bill. And Bill was the very best of all!

"Now," said Bill, "who do you think will be a good delegate from our bunk?" He searched the faces in front of him.

"Count me out," said Ben, quickly, "I'll be too busy with my camera."

"Count me out, too," said Jeff, "I'm no good at that kind of thing."

"I don't think I'd be the right one for such an important job," said Joshua, thoughtfully.

Michael looked at Joshua. Why couldn't Joshua be a delegate? "Why not?" he said out loud. "You'd make a wonderful delegate from our bunk."

Joshua's voice was firm. "I think you ought to be the one, Michael. You have good ideas and you're not afraid to speak up."

Steven wondered why the boys hadn't suggested him as the

delegate. He had good ideas and he'd make the other delegates do things his bunkmates would like. He decided to speak up. "How about me? I'm a good athlete and if I'm chosen, think of the breaks we could get in baseball and swimming."

The boys looked at Steven in surprise. Bill's eyes roamed from face to face. He decided to say nothing. Where would the discussion lead? He waited.

Michael swallowed the words that rushed to his lips. Steven had no right to talk like that! A delegate had to think of the good of the whole camp—not of the breaks he could get for his bunk. Besides, breaks have to be earned. At least that's what Daddy always said. Michael didn't say what he was thinking. Somehow, he knew Steven wouldn't like to be criticized. Besides, the boys might feel he thought he was better than Steven. A feeling of uneasiness came over him but he pushed it away. To Steven he said, "It's all right with me," knowing that it wasn't.

"Let's take a vote," suggested Joshua.

Bill gave them paper and pencil. When the votes were counted there were three for Michael and two for Steven.

With a quick jerk Steven opened his trunk and pretended to look for something inside. He didn't want the boys to see his disappointment. It was always like this. Whenever he wanted something he didn't get it. But not Michael, no, not Michael. Everything *he* wanted he grabbed without even trying. The boys had voted for Michael because "Kee Tov" had been chosen. Those dumb kids! They didn't fool him. Couldn't they see that he'd be a better delegate than Michael? Steven turned around and looked at them, his eyes flashing his thoughts. He decided to tell them just what he thought. He wasn't afraid to speak up. "It looks like Michael is the Number One boy around here," he said sharply, "first Kee Tov and now camp delegate!" His eyes accused his bunkmates of unfairness.

"Knock it off, Steven," warned Bill, his voice rising, "you'll get plenty of chances to show your stuff before too long!"

With an I-don't-care shrug Steven slid down under the blankets of his bunk, muttering to himself. There! He'd told them just what he thought. They'd be sorry when they discovered what he could do for them when it came to baseball. Wait and see! Let Michael be the delegate but he'd show them how to get the championships. They'd come begging him for favors. He was sure of it.

A lump swelled in Michael's throat. Now Steven wouldn't like him. He could see that already. Steven was plenty tough.

The soft note of taps sounded through the camp and Bill put out the lights. Silence settled over the bunk. Joshua broke the quiet with a question that had been on his mind all evening.

"Bill, why were the Jews chosen by God to receive the Torah? Does that mean that we are better than everyone else?"

Bill sat on the edge of his bed. "We Jews don't believe that at all, Joshua. And I don't think our ancestors believed it either. No one really knows why the Jews were chosen to receive the Torah. But—there is a story in the Midrash that may help to give an answer to that question. Like to hear it?"

"No!" came Steven's cross voice. "I want to go to sleep. I'm tired!" He twisted around in his bed and put his hands over his ears. Who wanted to hear a story someone made up a million years ago, anyway? The disappointment he felt filled every part of him. Why couldn't the boys have chosen him? He had wanted it so much!

The other boys were instantly wide awake. "Yes!" they shouted over Steven's "No."

"I'll talk softly so we won't disturb Steven," said Bill, looking at Steven's hunched-up shape under the blanket. He'd have to speak to Steven alone the next day and try to find out why he was so upset.

"The Rabbis say that before God offered the Torah to the Jews," began Bill in a low voice, "He came to the children of Esau. 'Will you accept the Torah?' he asked them.

" 'What is written in it?' asked the children of Esau.

" 'Thou shalt not murder,' God told them.

" 'That would be impossible. We cannot accept the Torah—we make our living by killing,' they replied.

"God then approached the children of Ishmael, asking them if they would be willing to accept the Torah. They, too, wanted to know what it contained.

" 'Thou shalt not steal,' came God's answer.

" 'But our lives depend on stealing,' they said. 'We cannot accept the Torah.'

"God then went to every nation and tribe on the earth offering the Torah to them. But each one refused it. Finally God came to the children of Israel.

" 'Will you accept the Torah?' He asked them.

" 'What is written in it?' they asked.

" 'In the Torah are 613 laws that you must promise to obey. You will have a great responsibility thrust upon your shoulders. It will be a difficult task for you to follow My laws, for you must spend your lives serving Me, by loving and serving your fellow man.'

"And the Midrash tells us that the children of Israel were quick to reply, 'Na-aseh V'nishma—All that the Torah has said we will do and we will hear.' "

Bill saw Steven twisting about in his bunk. "Loving and serving your fellow man," Bill repeated for Steven's benefit, "is an important part of obeying God's laws. That's the only way to keep the world that God made for us a good world. Kee Tov! Remember?"

Up over Steven's head went his blanket hiding him from sight. With a sigh, Bill said, "Enough talking for tonight, boys. Let's get some shut-eye. Don't forget to say your prayers. Goodnight."

In the darkness Steven was awake. Did Bill think he wasn't willing to do things for the other kids? That was the whole trouble! He *wanted* to help them all the time but they wouldn't let him. Everytime he thought of a good idea they squelched him just because he could do everything better than anyone else. And Michael was the worst one of all! He thought *he* was something special. Well, a surprise was in store for Michael. Just because Michael was the delegate, he needn't expect to be the big boss in their bunk. He'd see to that, all right! Just as Steven was listing all the things he planned to do to Michael, sleep hit him like a ton of bricks.

Michael glanced over at the sleeping Steven. Tossing and turning about in the bunk, Michael searched for a soft spot. How he wished Steven hadn't called him Number One boy! What if Steven picked on him and made the other kids hate him? He wished his father were there beside him. Dad would know what to do. But—Dad wasn't there. He'd have to face whatever happened all by himself. Good thing he had Marsha. Maybe she'd be able to help.

He decided to add an extra line to his prayers. "Please, God, help me find a way to make Steven my friend," he asked.

WHAT DO YOU THINK?

1. In the story, Steven gave his bunkmates two reasons why he thought he would make a good delegate. The first was because of his athletic ability.

    Do you think that skill in sports is enough reason to be chosen a leader? Why?

    The second reason was because he could get breaks for his bunkmates.

    Doesn't this show that Steven wanted to serve his bunkmates?

    Where was Steven's reasoning wrong?

    When you earn your own breaks, how do you feel inside?

2. Another story in the Midrash tells how King David was chosen by God to be a leader of his people. The Rabbis said that when David tended his flocks he always remembered to lead the baby lambs to pasture first so that they could eat the tenderest grass. Next, he allowed the older sheep to graze on the grass that was best for them. The remainder of the grass he gave to the oldest sheep. In this way, David saw that each animal in his flock was fed the food that was best for it.

How is this story like the one Bill told about Moses?

If you were choosing a leader, what kind of person would you want?

How will discussion of everyone's ideas help the group?

Would you rather go to a camp like Kee Tov or would you rather go to a camp where the adults choose what is best for you? Why?

3. *What advice would your Dad have given you if you had told him about Steven's behavior when he wasn't chosen delegate? How would you treat Steven?*

4. The next day Bill asked Steven why he was so angry when he wasn't chosen.

   What do you think Steven's answer was? If you were Bill, what advice would you give Steven?

5. *Why do you think Michael voted for Steven? Would you have voted for Steven? Why? Why not? Was Michael right in saying, "It's all right with me," or should he have said what was in his heart?*

6. *How did Steven fail to follow these words from the Talmud, "Let another praise you and not your own mouth"?*

7. *Did you ever feel as disappointed as Steven when you didn't get something you wanted very much? How did you work it out for yourself? Do you think Steven meant all the things he said to himself? Have you*

ever said things when you were angry that you really didn't mean? Does anger stop thinking?

8. *Where in the story did Steven fail to live up to the responsibilities of obeying God's laws according to the Midrash story that Bill told the boys about why the Jews were selected by God to have the Torah?*

9. *What do you think of Ben's and Jeff's reasons for not wanting to be delegates? How did they fail to take responsibility? How did Joshua prove he wanted to take the responsibility that God wants us to take toward our fellow man?*

4. SARA'S GHOST

Tamar was bent over her trunk searching for a clean pair of socks. Marsha was watching her. A pad of paper with a black horse sketched on the top caught Marsha's eye. The horse seemed to be racing across the page.

"Why, Tamar," cried Marsha, picking up the drawing, "what a dandy horse! Did you draw it?" Marsha held it out to admire its dashing lines.

Tamar looked at the sketch and wrinkled her nose. "That's a terrible horse!" she said, shaking her head, "the neck is too long. I love to draw—but my pictures never turn out the way I think about them in my head." Tamar snatched the picture out of Marsha's hand. Surprised, Marsha looked at Tamar. She didn't agree with Tamar at all. That horse looked real.

"Everything I do comes out like this—not quite right!" Tamar said to Marsha, shoving the drawing deep into her trunk.

"That's silly, Tamar. I wish I could draw like you do. When I try to draw a horse, it looks like a kangaroo." Marsha laughed at herself. "Do you go to art school?"

"My father teaches me. He's a wonderful artist. I want to be like him some day. But I'll never be able to draw like him—never in a million years." Tamar's shoulders drooped. She remembered her father telling her she had to have more patience. He kept saying that she was improving but she didn't really believe him. He just said those things because he was a father.

Marsha tried to make Tamar feel better. "But you have to believe you can do it. My daddy and mother are always telling Michael and me that you don't really know for sure whether you can do a thing until you try. Besides, you aren't even grown up yet. How do you know you won't be a famous artist like your father?"

"I just know!" Tamar replied. She was quiet for a long time after that.

How could Marsha know how she felt? She alone knew the truth. Did she get first prize at the art show in school last June? First prize! Huh! She didn't even get honorable mention and she had tried so hard. Tamar took a box of paper out of her drawer. "I have to write a letter to my mother," she said, bending over the paper. "Please excuse me."

Marsha could see that Tamar didn't want to talk any more. What a strange girl she was! Most of the time she didn't say much, but when she did—she was always talking against herself. Marsha couldn't understand Tamar at all.

Across the cabin Ann was smearing her nose with cold cream. Her nose looked like a blob of thick sour cream. Marsha giggled. "If I had some strawberries I'd dip them into your nose," she laughed. "Why are you smearing all that goo on your nose?"

"Freckles! Nasty old ugly freckles!" Ann swirled some more cream on her face. "So far it hasn't done any good. Some morning I'm going to get up at dawn and dip my freckly nose in dew. I read somewhere that dew is good for freckles." Ann flopped into bed wrinkling her creamy nose at Marsha. Both of them doubled up with laughter.

In the washroom Sara and Susan were crowding each other at the washbowl. With a hard shove Sara heaved Susan against the wall. "I was here first," she shouted, her cross voice filling the cabin.

"You can't push me around whenever you feel like it. I was here first and you know it!" Susan's words had tears in them.

Miriam hurried over to settle the argument. "Who was here first?" she asked.

"I was, Miriam. Honest, I was," insisted Susan.

Sara refused to answer. She glared at Miriam and Susan, and marched into the cabin, flashing her eyes at everyone as she passed. Miriam followed.

"Now what was that all about?" she asked Sara in a calm voice. "The washbowl can't possibly run away. It'll be here all summer."

The girls giggled but Sara didn't see anything funny. She shouted over the giggles, "I don't have to wash, you know. Not in this cheesy camp! What a place! No television! One washbowl for six people! I'll be glad when my mother and father come back and take me out of this silly camp!" Sara's scornful eyes swept the startled faces before her. Who was afraid? She hated every one of them and she didn't care who knew it! With a toss of her head she stared at them, defiantly, her hands on her hips.

Miriam's voice was low and firm. "Get washed, Sara. The washroom is clear now." Sara flounced through the cabin without a backward glance and slammed the door.

Wide eyes followed her. Sara had been acting like this all day. Miriam and the girls had tried several times to talk to her but each time Sara had made some excuse to leave. She refused to talk.

The girls found their tongues. Marsha was the first to speak. "That's not true—about camp I mean. Kee Tov is a wonderful camp and Sara's just mean and nasty to say all those horrible things." Marsha frowned at the closed door. She just knew that Sara was going to make trouble.

Susan exploded. "She's going to spoil our bunk! She doesn't like any of us. I tried to talk to her a dozen times today and she wouldn't even answer me."

"Me, too," added Ann. "Miriam, can't we ask Aaron to put her into another bunk?"

Tamar said nothing. Yes, it would be better if Sara switched bunks. Tamar was afraid Sara would fight with her, too.

"Wait a minute," interrupted Miriam, "I don't blame you for being upset—but—let's think a bit. A little while ago one of the campers suggested Ohavto as the Hebrew name for our camp. Ohavto means 'you shall love.' It comes from God's commandment to 'Love thy neighbor as thyself.' What does that mean to you?" Miriam paused to let her question sink in.

"It means you have to try to like people the way you want them to like you," said Marsha.

"But—what has that to do with Sara?" asked Ann.

"Just this," said Miriam, "would you like it if the tables were turned and Sara wanted to put *you* out of the bunk? Especially if you were unhappy and needed help?"

"But Sara doesn't want help," said Marsha, shaking her head, "we heard her say that, didn't we?"

Miriam continued patiently. "Sara wants to be loved. We all do. The trouble is—she doesn't know how to win love. She's so angry she can't think straight. And it's up to us to try to help her—if we can. Do you remember the story of the Golden Calf in the Bible?" Miriam looked at the closed door of the washroom before she began. "When Moses came down from Mt. Sinai with the Ten Commandments, he found his people worshipping the Golden Calf. Can you imagine how he must have felt? After all he had been through, guiding the people and preparing them to receive the Ten Commandments—here they were breaking the first one. Do you remember what he did?"

"He was so mad he threw the tablets on the ground and broke them into a thousand pieces," said Susan.

"Yet," continued Miriam, slowly, "he broke the tablets—he didn't smash the people. And even though the people had forgotten their promise to obey God's commandments, Moses still loved them. He pleaded with God to forgive the people, and he didn't stop pleading until God *did* forgive them."

Ann was still puzzled. "But what has the Golden Calf to do with Sara moving to another bunk? Maybe she'll be happier there."

"Just this," answered Miriam, "can't we be a little like God and Moses? Can't we try to love and forgive Sara, too? That takes doing—I know. What do you say? Are you willing to try?" The anxious tone in Miriam's voice made the girls realize how important it was to try to help Sara.

No one said a word. Miriam let them think about the problem for a little while. "And now, into bed, my pets," she said, with a smile, "we've a big day ahead of us tomorrow."

Tamar spoke suddenly. "Miriam, I've been wanting to ask you something but—" Tamar stopped. She didn't quite know how to ask her question. Miriam's look of interest made her try again. "I've been thinking about Gramps and how he told us about the Torah being like a Tree of Life. Could we make a real Tree of Life in the Arts and Crafts Shop?"

Miriam encouraged Tamar with a smile. "What do you mean?" she asked

All at once the idea seemed silly to Tamar. She dropped her eyes and swallowed her words.

"Tell us," urged Miriam, taking Tamar's hand. "Maybe your idea is good—besides we all want to hear it. Please, Tamar, tell us."

Tamar forced herself to talk. "Why can't we find a tree trunk and spread roots around the bottom. We could bore holes in the trunk and stick branches in the holes. Everytime someone did a good deed we could hang a piece of paper fruit on the branches with the person's name on it. Do you think that would be too hard to make?" Tamar saw the puzzled expressions of her bunkmates and bit her lips. There I go again, she thought. It's in my head but it won't come out right. If only she could make everyone understand what she was trying to describe.

Tamar was wrong. Miriam did understand. "That's a wonderful idea," she exclaimed, "and we can begin right here in bunk six. If we can help Sara, we'll be able to put lovingkindness on the Tree of Life."

Now the idea was beginning to take hold. Smiles spread over the girls' faces. They looked at Tamar with admiration.

Tamar's face warmed and she glanced gratefully at Miriam.

"We'll talk it over with Esther, the Arts and Crafts counselor," said Miriam, "and see what she thinks."

All at once Marsha remembered the horse Tamar had sketched. "Why don't you draw the Tree of Life so that you can make your idea clearer to Esther?" she suggested.

"I can't draw very well," objected Tamar, falling back into her habit of belittling herself again.

"You can, too! What about the horse in your trunk?" Marsha's eyes danced.

Susan giggled. "A horse in Tamar's trunk! Is it a big horse? Can I ride it? This I want to see!" Susan ran to Tamar's trunk.

"She drew a horse, silly," laughed Marsha.

Everyone laughed. Ann giggled so hard the blob of cream fell from her nose and plopped to the floor. Marsha scooped it up in her hand and plunked it back on Ann's nose. "Here," she laughed, "your freckles will get lonesome without this goo!"

Miriam broke into the merriment. "Susan, you're the camp delegate. Why don't you discuss Tamar's idea at the council? Perhaps the Tree of Life can be used for the whole camp."

Pleasure lit up Tamar's face. She could hardly believe that her idea was that good. She planned to write the good news to her father. Wouldn't it be wonderful if the Tree of Life were to

be used for the whole camp? On second thought, she'd better
wait. What if the council didn't like the idea? The old feeling
of discouragement took hold of her again. This time she
couldn't shake it. She gazed enviously at the other girls.
Why couldn't she be as jolly as they were? What a good time
they had. If only she could be like Marsha and Susan and Ann!

Sara came out of the washroom. She passed in frozen silence
without meeting anyone's eyes. The girls looked at Miriam and
spread their palms helplessly. Miriam put her fingers on her
lips. "Lights out!" she said, "good-night and sweet dreams.
Don't forget your prayers."

Marsha said her prayers to herself. All at once she missed her
parents. A lonely feeling came into her throat. If only she could
kiss them good-night! She closed her eyes and told herself not
to be such a baby. After all, she knew that God watched over
her here at Kee Tov just as He did at home.

The cabin was quiet. Suddenly, Miriam was awakened by a
gleam of light. Across the room Sara was holding a lighted
flashlight. Miriam tip-toed over to Sara's bed. She saw Sara
staring at the wall, her eyes wide open.

"You can't keep your flashlight on now, Sara," she said
softly. "The bugle means lights out!"

"I always have a light when I go to bed. I can't sleep without
one!" Sara's voice rose to a higher pitch and Miriam put her
finger to her lips.

"Sh-h-h, you're not at home now. There are others here with
you. Is it fair to disturb their sleep?"

"I don't care! I have to have a light!" Sara was determined to
have her own way. Besides, she *was* afraid of the dark. She had
been afraid since she was little.

Miriam took the flashlight, turned it off, and put it on the
table. "Go to sleep, Sara. Camp is a friendly place. There's
nothing to be afraid of here!"

Miriam smoothed the covers on Sara's bed and went back to
the other end of the cabin.

With a quick tug at the covers, Sara jumped out of bed. Snatching her blanket and the flashlight she ran over to Miriam. "If I can't sleep here with a light then I'll sleep on the porch with my flashlight on! You can't say that I'll bother the girls then!" Before Miriam could say anything, Sara raced outside.

On the porch a white shape leaped at her, knocking her over. Sara fled inside, wild with panic. "A ghost! A ghost!" she shouted, waking everyone with her screams. "There's a ghost on the porch! I saw it!"

The girls blinked. Marsha looked at the screen door. There, pawing frantically at the screen, was Lovon, the camp dog, a frightened look on his face. "Your ghost is Lovon," Marsha said, with disgust. "Why were you on the porch, anyway?"

Sara glared at Marsha and then at Lovon. "I hate that dog! What's he doing here?" Sara burst into tears. Miriam took her hand and led her back to bed.

Marsha ran out to comfort Lovon but he was nowhere to be seen.

Miriam sat on Sara's bed talking softly to her, trying to make her stop crying. "I told you you wouldn't like me," sobbed Sara. "Nobody does. Lovon had no right to frighten me half to death."

Miriam let Sara talk. She held Sara's hand in hers. "You remind me of a story, Sara. May I tell it to you?"

Sara didn't want to hear the story—not really—but she wanted Miriam to stay with her. "All right," she said, "if you want to tell it."

Miriam wiped away a tear that had rolled down Sara's cheek with a corner of the sheet and told her a story from the Talmud. "A company of people were traveling in a boat. Suddenly, one of the group took a drill and began to bore a hole in the bottom of the boat under his seat. The other people immediately raised a loud fuss. The man looked at them as if they were mad. 'Why are you so upset?' he asked. 'I bought a ticket, didn't I? And besides, it's under my own seat that I am boring this hole. So stop shouting.'"

Sara said, "What a crazy thing to do!"

Miriam smiled. "Not crazy—he just didn't think. Isn't our bunk like that boat in a way, Sara? If you think only of yourself we all suffer. If we work together and help each other, we'll all be happy. Doesn't that make good sense?"

Sara shrugged her shoulders and closed her eyes. Miriam waited until she was asleep. Sara's hand was clinging tightly to hers. The tired counselor slowly took her hand away and tiptoed away with a sigh.

Marsha decided to add another prayer to the one she had said.

"Please, God, help Sara to be good."

WHAT DO YOU THINK?

1. Tamar's idea for making the Tree of Life was accepted by the camp council for the entire camp. A huge tree painted silver stood upright in the dining-room in a tub of plaster. Thick paper roots spread in all directions. From the silver branches hung golden cardboard Torahs. Every Friday night after services in the chapel, Aaron awarded the Torahs near the flagpole. Torahs of service were given to the bunks who earned them. Even if only one member of a bunk earned the Torah, the whole bunk was honored.

   Do you think that having her idea used by the whole camp will help Tamar to build confidence in herself?

2. Long ago Rabbi Hillel said in the Talmud, "If I am not for myself, who will be for me?"

   How does this apply to Tamar? To Sara?

   How does Tamar show this idea? How does Sara?

Rabbi Hillel also said, "If I am only for myself, what good am I?"

How does this apply to Sara?

3. *Have you ever felt like Tamar—afraid to try something new, sure that you couldn't do it?*

   Did anyone encourage you to try? Who?

   What happened when you made the attempt? Did you discover that the task wasn't as difficult as you had imagined it?

   Have you ever helped a friend try to do something he was sure he couldn't do? How did your friend act when you encouraged him to try?

   Sometimes we keep on trying to do things after we have failed over and over again.

   Is it wiser to accept your failure, face up to it, and go on from there, or should you keep trying again?

   How can you decide whether you should try again or quit and go on to something else?

4. Tamar wanted with all her heart to be like her father.

   Have you ever felt like Tamar and wanted to be like someone else? Do you think you can be someone else? How can we copy what is good in others and still be true to ourselves?

5. Tamar was disappointed because she didn't get first prize in the art show.

   Have you ever had a disappointment like this especially when you tried hard? What did you do about it? Did you give up or did you make up your mind to try harder? What happened?

   If Tamar did the best she could she is always a winner.

   Can you explain this? Could it help Tamar get over her disappointment?

6. Every summer Sara and her family went to their summer cottage at Cape Cod. There Sara had a sailboat that she loved with all her heart. She had learned to sail it and she knew how to take care of it like a true sailor. It was one of the chief joys of her life. All winter Sara looked forward to the time when she could sail her beloved boat. Sara's family delayed telling her that she could not go to the Cape until just a day before camp because they knew she'd make a fuss. This sudden disappointment was partly the reason for Sara's actions.

   Do you think she had a good reason for behaving as she is now?

   When the girls and Miriam discover what is making Sara unhappy, do you think they will understand Sara better? Why is it important to try to understand other people? What does it tell us about loving our neighbor? One of the Rabbis in the Talmud once said, "Do not judge your neighbor until you have put yourself in his place." How does this help us to love others?

7. Sometimes unhappy people blame everybody and everything. They forget to blame themselves.

   Whom did Sara blame instead of herself?

   Have you ever had an experience like Sara's when your dearest dream was shattered? Did you face up to it and accept it or did you refuse to face it like Sara? How did you reason it out for yourself? Did someone help you? Who?

   Why was Miriam's story about the boat a good story to tell Sara?

8. List all the ways in the story that proved that Sara was thinking only of herself.

   How did Miriam's story about the Golden Calf help the girls to think about helping Sara?

   Have you ever had an experience when someone's selfishness caused you and others unhappiness?

What did you do about it? Were you afraid to speak up? Why?

9. Another proverb in the Talmud says, "Thou hast entered a city. Abide by its customs."

   How did Sara break this rule? How can you carry out this rule when you go visiting? When you are in school? When you are at play? When you are in your home?

10. A rabbi of long ago invited his students to a meal and served each a portion of soft tongue well cooked, and of tough tongue, half-raw. The students ate the soft tongue with gusto, but left the tough one untouched on their plates. The rabbi laughed and said, "Let this be a lesson to each of you. Just as you prefer the soft tongue to the tough one, so shall your own tongues be soft and tender toward each other when you speak to your neighbor."

   Who in the story has the soft tongue?

   How does this story help explain the Bible proverb, "A soft answer turns away wrath"?

11. Miriam asked the girls to be like God and Moses after the Jews had made the Golden Calf and forgive Sara. One of the campers had suggested B'tzalmo—"In His image" as a name for the camp.

   How did Miriam want the girls to show that they were created in God's image? If everyone, even someone we don't like, is created in God's image then do we have an excuse for hating anyone? Does this help you to understand why Miriam thought B'tzalmo was such an important idea in our religion?

5. DREADFUL FRIDAY!

Michael lay awake remembering all that had happened during the past two weeks.

Gramps' suggestion that a Hebrew name be given to each bunk had been accepted by the camp council. Michael's bunk was named *Emes*—truth. Outside of each cabin were boards on which the names had been painted. Michael smiled to himself. Marsha's bunk was called *S'Goolo*—treasure. Lovon had licked off some of the paint before it had dried, so for a little while Marsha's bunk had been called "Goo." What a joke that had been! A huge sign, bearing the name "Kee Tov," swung at the entrance of the camp. Funny thing! Everyone felt as if Kee Tov had been the camp's name all the time.

What a wonderful camp! And Emes was the very best bunk of all. At first Michael had worried about Steven but to his surprise Steven had recovered from his disappointment. Now he and Steven were good friends. Steven was a wonderful athlete. When he hit a ball out into the baseball field—that ball really traveled. He did everything better than anyone else. Michael admired him. How he wished he could play ball like Steven.

Perhaps he would before long. Steven was helping him with his batting. He was really a good friend! Of course, you had to understand Steven and watch out not to get him angry. Then he said things that hurt. Bill was forever warning him to think before he spoke. And Steven *was* trying. But when things didn't go his way, he tore into you like all get-out. Still and all, Steven was good company. Michael really liked him—well, *most* of the time.

The Tree of Life floated into Michael's thoughts. Some of the bunks had already earned Torahs. The Giborim in B'tzalmo had saved a cat marooned on a tall tree near their cabin. The frightened cat had scrambled to the very top. No amount of coaxing could budge it. It stayed there for two days. B'tzalmo worried and worried afraid the cat would starve. Finally, they dragged a tall ladder to the tree, and one of the boys climbed up and rescued the cat. Printed on their golden Torah was: "To B'tzalmo—for mercy." When he awarded the Torah, Aaron said that the boys were really living up to their name, "in His image." They had shown mercy, just as God shows mercy to all His creatures.

Everyone in the Na-arim bunk, Ohavto, had passed the Junior Life-Saving Test. Each girl had made up her mind to help the other in her spare time. Their Torah said, "To Ohavto —for lovingkindness." Aaron had said that they, too, were living up to their name, "you shall love," by showing lovingkindness to each other.

But Emes had no Torah. When the boys complained to Bill that nothing ever happened to them, Bill said comfortingly, "Your time will come. The summer's young yet."

A mother robin, dangling a fat worm, hopped onto Michael's window sill. She cocked her head as if to say, "Get up! Get up! The whole world's waiting for you!" At the same time, Michael saw Bill roll out of bed. "All right, boys, up and out—all of you." He slapped each blanket lump as he passed to the back. One by one the boys sat up, stretching their arms and blinking sleepy eyes. That is, all except Ben. He buried his nose deeper in the pillow. Bill shook his shoulder. "Rise and shine, Buddy."

"Go away!" came Ben's muffled voice.

The boys decided to help Bill. Jeff sat on Ben's back, Michael threw a pillow at his head, and Steven tickled the soles of his feet. Ben simply *had* to defend himself against the attack. With a deep sigh he rolled out of bed. He pulled his sports shirt over his head and got stuck. "Someone help me!" he shouted from inside the shirt. Michael came to the rescue. "That's a dumb way to get dressed," he said, unbuttoning the top buttons so Ben could get his head through. Ben grinned. "It's the best way there is, Smarty. This way I save time. And I have less to wash, too."

"You're not saving my time," said Michael, good naturedly.

In the washroom Jeff pounded on his tooth-paste tube. No paste! "Let me use your tooth-paste, Josh, please?" he called, "mine's as dry as the moon."

Bill watched Josh hand his tube to Jeff and frowned. "You wouldn't have to borrow, Jeff, if you hadn't wasted yours squirting space rockets on the mirror."

"Josh doesn't mind, Bill. I'll pay him back," said Jeff, his mouth full of tooth-paste.

"It's all right, Bill," said Josh, quickly. "I've tons of the stuff."

"That's not the idea, Josh. Jeff is always borrowing and it's a bad habit."

Jeff rinsed his mouth. "If anyone needs anything I have, I always let him borrow mine."

Bill eyed Jeff. "Yes, but when you borrow, it's like making your neighbor do your work for you. If you thought ahead you wouldn't have to borrow. When you were at the canteen yesterday getting your candy, why didn't you buy some tooth-paste?" Bill rumpled Jeff's curly hair.

Jeff nodded. "O.K. I'll get some today—I promise."

Ben was making his bed. He glared at the sheet as if it were a bitter enemy. It slopped over on one side with too much lap at the bottom. He shook his head with disgust. How could one silly sheet get so lop-sided? Oh, well, he'd put the sheet on any old way. But Bill was watching. Walking over to Ben, he said, "Here we go again! Watch carefully, Ben. Perhaps this time you'll get the trick."

With a groan, Ben helped Bill pull off all the bed clothes. "Do you think I'll ever learn, Bill?" he asked, with a sigh.

"Watch!" repeated Bill, "you're bound to get it."

Steven finished his bed. He stepped back to admire its smoothness. When he saw Bill helping Ben again he burst out before he could stop himself, "Golly, Ben, last week we lost the cleanliness Torah because of your sloppy bed. Are you going to make us lose it again this week? Are you?"

Ben shrugged. "Everyone can't be perfect like you. I never made a bed in my life before I came to Kee Tov."

"But we're working together for the good of the bunk, aren't we?" Steven's temper flared. "Can't you learn to do your job without leaning on Bill?"

Bill's jaw tightened. "Quit it, Steven. Ben wants to do his job well just as much as you do. Let's help him instead of getting angry. And Steven, Ben doesn't lean on me. My job is to help all of you whenever I can—and I'm glad to do it."

"O.K. Bill," said Steven, already ashamed of his outburst. How he wished he could be calm like Bill. Bill always saw the other fellow's point of view. But just the same, Ben wasn't trying hard enough. He could tell.

Bill tried a new approach. "Look, Ben, you're a cameraman. When you take a picture, you line up what you want to snap with your camera eye, don't you?" Bill caught Ben's interest as well as the other boys'. They crowded around him. "Use your eyes like the camera lens and make believe the sheet is the picture you want to take. Then line up the sheet. It'll come out straight, you'll see. Here, try it again."

Bill was right. As soon as Ben used the camera angle, the

sheet fell into place. For the first time Ben was pleased with his bed. "Thanks, Bill," he said, gratefully.

"I'm going to try that trick, too, it really works!" said Michael. All the boys agreed—including Steven.

Jeff plunked himself in front of Bill holding a glass of water. "I bet I can stay under water for three minutes," he laughed.

"Impossible!" said Bill.

Jeff held the water over his head. "Time me!" Bill pretended to punch Jeff's stomach. "I always fall for your gags."

Bill looked up to see Ben dancing around the cabin with a broom in his arms. A pair of false teeth jiggled on his hair. He bumped into Steven and the false teeth fell into Steven's open laundry bag.

"Hey! Do you want me to send your teeth to the laundry?" With a wild shriek, Ben snatched the teeth from the bag before Steven could pull the cord.

They heard the blast of the bugle announcing breakfast.

"Quit the fooling, fellows," said Bill. "After breakfast we've work to do. And it's our turn to set the tables for supper. Friday! Remember?"

"Dreadful Friday!" came loud groans from all around the cabin.

"Here we go again!" laughed Bill. "I quote God's Fourth Commandment, 'For six day shall you labor . . .' "

" 'And do all your work,' " chorused the boys in one voice.

"Is that your favorite commandment, Bill?" asked Joshua, "you always say it to us."

"It's very important," said Bill, "God created a good world —Kee Tov. Well, God also created work. So work must be good, too. That's how Jews have always felt about it. They said that God Himself was the first worker. He made the world. If God can work so can we. To the Jew, work is a *mitzvah*, a commandment, God's commandment."

The boys looked at each other and chuckled. "Dreadful Friday!" they shouted again.

"So, let's pitch in, all of us, with good will and the work will get done twice as fast," Bill grinned.

Ben announced, "First let's eat. My stomach is tickling my ribs. I need food before I can tackle all that work!"

After breakfast, Bill assigned the work. Michael was the sweeper, Steven the duster, Joshua was in charge of the wash-bowl, Ben had to clean the cabin grounds, and Jeff was the floor washer. They set to work with a will.

"I'll be back," said Bill, who was preparing his sermon for the Friday night services. "And when I return I'll inspect, so don't skirt the dirt!"

"I feel like a five-star general," said Michael, marching around the room with the broom against his shoulder.

"Ditto!" agreed Steven, flicking his dust cloth at Michael's broom-gun.

Michael glanced at a pail of water standing in the middle of the room. He looked around for Jeff. No Jeff! "Where's the spaceman?" he asked Steven.

Steven threw his dust cloth on the floor. "Leave it to Jeff—he always manages to be somewhere else when there's a job to do!" Michael could feel Steven's rising anger. Aloud, he said, "He'll be back. Maybe he went to the canteen to get some tooth-paste." Michael bent to push the pail to one side. Steven wouldn't let him touch it.

"You're a softie, Michael. Leave the pail where it is. If Jeff thinks we'll do his work for him like we did last week, he's mis-taken. This pail is going to wait for him just where he left it!" Once and for all, Steven was going to teach Jeff a lesson. Just because Michael was always willing to do things for the boys, Jeff had no right to take advantage. Fair is fair!

Joshua came out of the washroom and walked toward Michael. "Will you see if I cleaned all the spots, Michael, please?" he asked. Before anyone could warn him, there was a clatter and a crash. Grabbing at the air, Joshua sprawled on the floor, one foot in the pail of water. The floor came up to hit him on the head, knocking him out for a moment. With shouts of alarm, Michael and Steven rushed to Josh. All of them slipped and crashed down in the mess.

The noise brought Bill and Ben streaking into the cabin. It took a while to untangle the wet boys. Bill felt around for broken bones and then went to find Jeff. He found him in the science museum playing with some new-born hamsters.

Jeff pointed to the tiny animals. "Look, Bill, they're so small they can fit into a teaspoon."

Bill looked grimly at Jeff. "That pail you left in the middle of the floor sent Joshua sprawling and knocked him out." Jeff's face paled and his heart went into a power dive. "He isn't hurt, is he, Bill? He's all right, tell me he's all right!" Jeff clutched Bill with frantic fingers.

"He'll be fine," said Bill, "no thanks to you!"

Jeff hung his head.

"Why is it, Jeff, that you always maange to be interested in things at the wrong time? This isn't the first time you've shirked your work and wandered off on one of your nature trips." Bill's voice bored into Jeff, forcing him to lift his head.

Jeff spread his hands helplessly. "I don't know. I guess I don't think. I love science so much I forget everything else when I have a chance to follow it up."

"Poor excuse! Would you like it if the others left you their work and ran off whenever they felt like it?"

"But I didn't mean it. When I think of what might have happened to Josh—golly, I feel like a heel."

"That's not the idea. You have to have consideration for everyone—not only for the blind. You have to do your own work. That's part of living together—here at camp, at home, at school, everywhere!"

Jeff felt a hard knot tightening inside him. He couldn't find a word to say.

"Remember, Jeff, work is a commandment, God's commandment. When you learn to do your share of the work, you'll make the people around you happier, and yourself, too! Think about that!"

When they returned to the cabin Bill and Jeff found Michael mopping the floor. The silence in the cabin fairly shouted at Jeff. "I'll finish mopping, the floor," he said, taking the mop from Michael. Turning to Joshua, he said, "I'm sorry, Josh. I didn't think. I'm glad you weren't hurt." But Jeff's apology didn't change the accusing faces of his bunkmates. His stomach flipped over and landed with a thud. They'd never forgive him! Suddenly, the full meaning of his action hit him like a rocket. He mopped the floor, not daring to raise his eyes.

Steven lashed out at Jeff. "You never think of the other guy. You think only of Jeff, 'Me, myself, and I!' That's your motto! What if Joshua had broken his neck?" Steven's eyes drilled into Jeff. Joshua listened to the tongue-lashing and wished Steven would stop. Josh felt as if *he* were to blame. If he weren't blind this wouldn't have happened. If only he could have been able to see that pail! Anyway, Steven wasn't the boss. Why didn't he stop acting like one? Josh decided to speak up. "I'm not sore at Jeff. Let's forget it!"

Jeff finished mopping the floor and left the cabin to hang up the mop. Bill waited until he was outside before he began to talk. "Let's not be too hard on Jeff. He's sorry and I think he's had a good lesson. And Steven, why don't you let me handle the scoldings around here? It's my job!"

"But I just wanted to make sure Jeff would be more careful next time."

"It sounded more like anger to me. The Talmud says that when the wrong-doer begs forgiveness it is the duty of the injured party to forgive! Joshua was the one Jeff hurt and he was the first one to forgive Jeff. If he can, I guess we can, too."

The boys were quiet as Bill continued. "It's a mitzvah to work and it's a mitzvah to forgive the one who is truly sorry. Jeff is going to think twice from now on. I don't think he'll shirk his work again." He looked at his watch. "Let's finish up the work now. We're due in the mess hall in ten minutes."

Just then, Ben snapped his fingers with a groan, "Now why didn't I have my camera ready? What a beautiful shot that mess on the floor would have made!" Everyone laughed.

Soon they were on their way to the dining hall.

Each boy had four tables to set. Joshua sat next to Bill folding napkins.

"I've got an idea," said Bill. "When I say 'Go,' set your tables as fast as you can. When you finish I'll inspect. The one who finishes first gets my dessert tonight. But remember, the tables have to be in apple-pie order."

Michael laughed. "Why does everyone always say 'apple-pie order'? Why not 'lemon-pie order' or 'cherry-pie order'?"

Ben gave Michael a poke in the ribs. "Stop!" he cried. "You're breaking my heart with all that not-to-be-had food!"

"Ready!" shouted Bill.

The boys bent to a running position.

"On your mark!" said Bill, dragging out the words.

"Get—set!" he said, even more slowly than before.

The boys groaned.

"And uh—and uh—and uh—go!" The "go" exploded like a firecracker.

They scurried around like beetles. The promise of extra dessert spurred Ben to rush as he had never rushed before. "Why didn't I bring my roller skates?" he shouted to Bill as he scooted by his bench.

Jeff worked quietly. He didn't care whether he won or not. Unhappiness filled every part of him. How was he going to prove he was sorry?

In spite of Ben's speed, he was soon outdistanced by Steven and Michael. They were tied, each getting his knives and forks for the last table. Suddenly, Ben bumped into Steven causing the silverware in his hands to fall crashing to the floor. Steven had to run back to gather more knives and forks. Michael won.

"That's not fair!" shouted Steven, stamping his foot at Michael and glaring at Ben. "Ben made me trip! Nobody should win!" He turned to Bill. "You saw what happened. Should anyone win?"

Bill tossed the problem into Michael's lap. "It's up to Michael. He'll have to decide."

Michael was standing near the Tree of Life. The golden Torahs dangled before his eyes. He didn't know what to say. Would Steven really have won if he hadn't been tripped? He could see Steven's face getting redder and redder. Another explosion was on the way. Michael didn't want another argument. There had been enough trouble that morning in the cabin. For the sake of peace, he said, quickly, "All right, Steven. No one wins." To Bill he called, "I guess you'll get to eat your dessert after all."

Bill came over to Michael. "The United Nations couldn't have done better," he said, smiling. A look of understanding passed between them.

The kitchen door opened and Joe appeared with a bowl of apples.

"Come and get it!" he called.

Ben was the hungriest. He ate his way through the apple as if a man from Mars were chasing him. Starting at the North Pole he blasted his way in a straight line down to the South Pole, eating the skin, core, and seeds. Michael watched him with admiration. "Look boys," he laughed, "Ben's planting apple seeds in his stomach. Some day he's going to wake up and find two apple trees growing out of his ears."

Ben slapped his thighs. "What an imagination!" he cried, doubling up with laughter.

WHAT DO YOU THINK?

1. Michael missed his parents. It wasn't so bad when he was busy during the day—but at night when he went to bed and in the morning when he arose he wanted

them near him. He didn't complain because he didn't want the boys to call him a sissy. One day, while he was helping Gramps in the nursery, he let his longing for his parents slip out and he told Gramps how he felt. Gramps said that missing his parents was a natural feeling. It showed that Michael loved them. Gramps said, "You are obeying the Fifth Commandment, Michael, 'Honor your father and mother.'"

What do you think Gramps meant?

Do you miss your parents when you go away from them for a while?

Do you think a child is a sissy who does?

What are some of the ways in which you can honor your parents? At home? In school? At play?

2. Steven said that Michael shouldn't do Jeff's job for him.

   Do you agree with Steven? Do you agree with Michael?

   Do you think people take advantage of those people who are willing to do the extra work? Why?

   Has anyone ever taken advantage of you in this way? How did you feel?

   Have you ever taken advantage of someone who was willing to do your work? How did you feel? Why is taking advantage wrong? Is it always wrong to help someone with his work?

3. Bill inspected all the tables after they were set. When he saw Ben's tables he was disgusted. The silverware had been dumped in an untidy heap. Ben grinned at Bill and said, "The smell from the kitchen made me rush. A car can't run on an empty gas tank, can it?" Bill answered, "Excuses! Excuses! How can you be satisfied with this kind of a lick-and-a-promise work?"

   What did Bill mean?

   How was Ben running away from his problem?

   Have you ever done sloppy work because you were in a hurry to do something else?

How did you feel when it was pointed out to you?

Why is it important to do proud work at home? At school? With your friends?

How do you feel when people praise you for a job well done?

Why can't you respect the fellow who does sloppy work?

When should we listen to excuses? When should we not listen to excuses?

4. Maimonides was a famous Jewish physician and scholar in Cairo, Egypt, about 750 years ago. History tells us that after he finished his duties as the court doctor he came home and cared for all the poor people who had gathered in his house. He found time to write books and he wrote letters to people all over the world helping them with their problems. One thing he said was, "If you have been hired to work, do what you are told even if you don't like the work."

   How did Maimonides follow his own advice? Look up the story of his life and decide how he did it.

5. In the Bible God made this promise to Isaac: "I will bless you and increase your seed." Yet the rabbis of later years pointed out that Isaac planted and worked with all his heart in his field. The rabbis said Isaac felt that "Blessings cannot come except through the work of one's own hands."

   Do you agree with the rabbis? Why? Why not?

   Can you think of a time when hard work brought you or someone you know great happiness?

   Why is work important even if it doesn't bring us exactly what we want?

6. *What is the difference between the way Bill spoke to Ben about his bed and the way Steven did? What is the difference between patience and anger? Why is anger like Steven's usually bad? Why is patience like Bill's good? Tell us about some of your experiences with angry or patient people. Is anger always wrong*

and never right? Is patience always right and never wrong? Have you ever experienced good anger and bad patience? How did Michael show patience with Steven when he agreed with him about no one winning Bill's dessert?

7. The Midrash tells us that Noah invented the plow, the scythe, and the hoe. Before Noah, the people worked the land with their bare hands. Noah turned farming into a more agreeable task. He was the first of many who helped people down through history.

Can you think of people who by their hard work helped mankind?

How did their efforts make the world a better place in which to live?

How can you by your work make the world a good place in which to live?

Let every child in the class choose a person whose work has proved valuable to humanity in our day and report to the class.

At the end of each report ask the question, How did they obey God's mitzvah, "For six days shalt thou labor—and do all thy work"?

6. GRAMPS

During rest hour Jeff decided to go to the Thinking Place. Bill had told him to stop worrying and Joshua had forgiven him. But the other boys were giving him the quiet treatment. Operation Deep Freeze! They had hardly spoken to him all day. He kicked a clump of earth and sent it flying in a spray of dust.

In the pine grove he met Sara Miller sitting on a bench, staring off into space. The dark cloud on her face told Jeff that Sara was unhappy, too. Walking over to her he greeted her with "Hi! You in trouble, too?" He sat down beside her.

"I'm always in trouble," Sara said, scornfully. "I hate this camp! Don't you?"

Jeff stared at her. Hate Kee Tov! Golly, there wasn't a better camp in the world! "There's nothing wrong with Kee Tov," he said. "You can't blame the camp if you're in trouble!"

"What a place! Work! Work! Work! Dusting and cleaning and scrubbing every day of the week, over and over again. What's good about a camp like this?"

At that instant they looked up to see Gramps standing over them holding a big book in his hand. He smiled kindly. "I couldn't help overhearing your voices. You sound upset. Can I help?"

Without a word the children made room. Reaching into his pocket Gramps pulled out a package of fruit drops. With a deep chuckle he offered the candy to each of them. Popping one into his own mouth he waited for them to speak.

Sara spoke first. "No one in this camp likes me," she said, with a shrug. Jeff nodded miserably. "No one in my bunk likes me, either," he added.

"Well, I do," Gramps said, promptly, twinkling his blue eyes at them.

The understanding in Gramps' face untied the hard knot in Jeff's stomach. He found himself telling Gramps everything. Sara listened quietly, wondering what Gramps would say.

"Well, from where I sit, I'd say that your bunkmates like *you*. It's what you *did* that they don't like. Isn't that it?"

"Yes—but—" Jeff hesitated.

"You have a problem, Jeff, no doubt about that! Let's dig into this book of the Talmud and see if we can find a story to help you solve your problem." Gramps opened the book and flipped the pages. All at once he snapped his fingers. "I have it, just the right one. Listen! One of the Rabbis in the Talmud, Rabbi Meir, knew his neighbors were guilty of many wicked deeds. He pleaded with them to stop their wickedness but they laughed at him and continued to be bad. Rabbi Meir was so upset that he prayed they would be removed from the earth."

"But it's not right to pray that way," interrupted Jeff.

"Of course, it's not," agreed Gramps, "but rabbis make mistakes too. Listen! Rabbi Meir had a wise wife named Beruriah. When she heard her husband praying in that way, she said, 'The Bible seems to say, "Let sinners depart from the world and the wicked will be no more." But we should read it as, Let *sin* depart from the world and the wicked will be no more. So, dear husband, would it not be better if you pray that sinners will repent of their sins? Then will their wickedness stop.' "

"Did Rabbi Meir take his wife's advice?" asked Sara, breaking her silence.

Gramps chuckled. "He must have listened, Sara, because we think he wrote the story in the Talmud and gave his wife all the credit."

"I wish my bunkmates felt like Beruriah," said Jeff. "I told the boys I was sorry and I promised I'd never shirk my work again. Do you think they'll forgive me—ever?"

Gramps patted Jeff's shoulder. "Of course they will! And do you know how I know? Because you've taken the first step already. You're sorry for what you did and now all you have to do is prove you mean it. It won't take long for them to believe in you again."

Jeff felt better. The determination to change filled every part of him. He'd show them!

Gramps turned toward Sara. "Do you want to tell me what's bothering you?"

"It won't do any good," said Sara, in a tired voice. Her loneliness reached out to touch Gramps' heart when she added, "You'll think like the others."

"Try me and see," encouraged Gramps. "You haven't given me a chance."

Sara searched his face. Would Gramps understand? Could she tell him about her boat and her family? Would he be able to understand why she was so unhappy? Nobody wanted to understand her point of view. Instead, Sara found herself saying, "Everything I do is wrong. This morning I just didn't feel like cleaning my share of the bunk. Marsha loves to clean. She makes a game of it. So I offered her a quarter to do my work for me. Marsha wouldn't take the money. She said her mother wouldn't like it. But she did my work for me, anyway. When Miriam found out, she sent me to the Thinking Place to think about what I had done." Sara's lower lip quivered. "If Marsha was willing, what difference does it make to Miriam as long as the work was done?"

Gramps' hands touched the cover of the Talmud. He was silent for a long minute. Finally he spoke. "That's not the way God wants us to work, Sara. When Moses was leading the Jews out of Egypt he used to hold court each day, from morning until late at night, trying to settle his people's problems. Jethro, Moses' father-in-law, said to him, 'My son, you are working too hard. You need all your strength to help the people receive the Torah.'

" 'But only I can judge the people,' objected Moses. 'They need me.'

" 'They do. But you need them to share the work. Choose some honest men you can trust and appoint them as judges over the people. Let them care for the every-day problems. Special cases they can bring to you to settle. This will free you to do other tasks. In this way everyone will share in the work and they will all be much happier.' " Gramps stretched his legs. "Do you think Jethro's advice helped Moses?" Gramps asked the two children.

"I suppose so," said Sara, thoughtfully, "but how did Jethro have the courage to talk to Moses like that? Wasn't Moses the wisest man in those days?"

Sara's question surprised Gramps but he was pleased when she asked it.

"In the Talmud the Rabbis ask, 'Who is wise?' The answer is, 'He who learns from all men.' Moses was wise because he was willing to learn from all men. That's just as true for us today. To get back to your problem, Sara—was it fair to Marsha to let her do your work even though she wanted to? Isn't that putting too much of a load on her shoulders?"

Sara didn't answer but Jeff did. He looked at Gramps as if he understood his own problem at last.

"That's my trouble. I left my share of the work for the others. What a dope I've been!"

Gramps objected to the word, "dope." "We all make mistakes. And you can't call my favorite spaceman a dope! I won't allow it!" Gramps brushed away a lock of hair hanging over Jeff's eye.

"Please tell us another story," said Sara, to Gramps' astonishment. "I like the way you tell them."

Gramps' eyes gleamed with mischief. "About work?" he teased.

"If it's a good story—it can even be about work." The way Sara tossed her head made Gramps and Jeff burst into laughter.

"I have a good one this time—about work. Do you still want to hear it?"

"Yes," repeated Sara, crinkling her nose at Gramps' merry face.

"When Moses received the Ten Commandments on Mount Sinai he decided to build a house for them. They needed a special house that could be carried wherever the people traveled. The people needed to see the Law before them so they would know that God was with them every step of the journey. Here again, Moses didn't do all the work himself. His chief architect was Bezalel, the first Jewish artist in the Bible. He said to the people, 'Let all whose heart is willing come to build the tabernacle and furnish it.' Everyone who was willing came to work and each brought a special gift. Can you imagine how happy they were to share in the building of God's house?"

"Did everyone have a willing heart, Gramps?" asked Sara.

"We don't know that. But I'd like to think that everyone had a willing heart. There are always people, then and today, too, who say 'No' when they are asked to share the work. Like you and Jeff, for instance." Gramps gazed down into their faces and said the last words slowly.

"Not me, not any more," came Jeff's quick reply. "I've reformed. You'll see."

"I believe you, Jeff. And now—let's have some more refreshments," said Gramps, offering the candy to the children. "My throat's dry."

Jeff chuckled. "You have to wet your whistle, Gramps."

A roar of laughter spilled out into the air. It came from Sara. "She laughed!" cried Gramps.

"She laughed!" echoed Jeff.

A big grin spread over Sara's face. For the first time since she had come to Kee Tov she felt good. She wished she could stay with Gramps forever. He liked her. She just knew it.

"Gramps," she said, "all that happened in the Bible a million years ago. It's different now. If I do extra work at home I get paid. Mother always gives me money. The people in the Bible were never paid."

"They were paid, Sara. Sometimes with money, but sometimes with something much more important. Knowing they had shared in building a house for the Ten Commandments was their best reward. They found happiness in serving God and each other."

Sara was still not convinced. "But nowadays we don't have to do heavy work like washing and scrubbing. We have a maid to do all that dirty work at home. Ugh!"

Gramps answered Sara with a question.

"Did Moses feel that way? He was a prince in Egypt and his adopted mother gave him everything he wanted. He had gold and silver, he lived in a splendid palace, and he had slaves to obey his every command. He was next to the Pharaoh in importance. Yet the Rabbis in the Midrash tell us that when Moses saw his people working as slaves, making bricks from clay and straw, he pitched in and worked along with them, helping to bear their heavy loads. Moses didn't think he was too good for what you call the 'dirty work.' What do you say to that?"

"But this is my vacation. I need a rest!" Sara argued.

Jeff wasn't as patient with Sara as Gramps. He waved away her complaint with a grunt. "Who works hard at Kee Tov? There's oodles of fun every minute!"

"And another thing," continued Gramps, "the Talmud tells us that while the Rabbis studied Torah, they also worked. No kind of work was too hard for them. Rabbi Akiba was a shepherd, Hillel a woodchopper. There was a shoemaker, a tailor, a baker, a carpenter, a silk dealer, and even a gravedigger. 'Acquire a trade with the Torah,' they said and they followed their own advice. They honored all kinds of work. For them, studying the Torah and working at the same time was a happy partnership."

Jeff peeked at Gramps' watch. "Golly, I have to blast back and get shined up for Shabos." He jumped to his feet. "Thanks Mr. Talmud! You knew exactly how to straighten me out. I'm going to try to do better, you'll see." With a good-bye to Sara, he grinned gratefully at Gramps and ran off through the pines.

The thought of returning to her cabin filled Sara with dread. She said in a whisper, "Can I stay a while longer?" The lonely note in Sara's voice reached deep into Gramps' heart. He took her hand in his.

"Of course," he answered.

And then the unhappiness in Sara exploded. She told Gramps everything. Her eyes sparkled with excitement when she talked about her boat. They brimmed with tears when she told him how her family had left her. Gramps nodded his head with sympathy, and tried to help her again.

"One of my favorite quotations in the Talmud is 'I am a child of God and my neighbor is a child of God. My work is in the city and his work is in the fields. I rise early in my work and he rises early in his. He boasts not of his work and I boast not of mine. And if he says that I do great things and he small, I ask, "Have we not learned that it matters not whether a man does much or little if only he directs his heart to serve God?"'" Gramps looked down into Sara's sad face. "It depends on where your heart is. For some people, sailing is work and for others it's fun. For some people, travel is work and for others it's vacation. As for camp—it all depends where you put your heart. Will you think about that, Sara?" Gramps gave Sara another hug and added, "And I like you very much."

Sara's face lit up with pleasure.

At that instant Lovon sauntered into the pine woods and trotted toward them. Sara jumped to her feet. To Gramps she shouted, "Thanks for the candy!" To Lovon she shouted, "Don't come near me—you mean old dog!" And off she raced.

"Come and see me again," called Gramps after her flying figure.

Lovon nuzzled his head in Gramps' lap. When Gramps scratched his ear he yipped with pleasure.

"Sara is so mixed-up," said Gramps to Lovon. "I wish I could help her. Deep down underneath I know there's a wonderful girl."

Lovon wagged his tail as if he understood.

The wind whispered in the pine trees and ruffled Gramps' snowy hair. He thought of the new name Jeff had given him and chuckled out loud. "Mr. Talmud," he murmured, opening the pages of his book. "I like that."

WHAT DO YOU THINK?

1. If Gramps had time he could have told Jeff and Sara the story of Nehemiah. In 538 B.C.E., King Cyrus conquered Babylonia. He allowed the Jews to return to Palestine to rebuild their Temple in Jerusalem. Can you imagine the joyful return to their homeland after being away about fifty years? The Bible tells us that Nehemiah, the cupbearer to the king, left his comfortable home in Persia, and came to Palestine to help his people become a nation again. He set himself the task of rebuilding the wall around Jerusalem. To the people he said, "Let us rise up and build," and so they strengthened their hands for the good work.

   Each group was given part of the wall to build. They came from all walks of life—rich and poor, farmers and judges, men from the villages. All came to do their share. Enemies arose who tried to destroy the work but the people worked with swords at their sides and trumpets to sound the alarm in case of sudden attack. "The people had a mind to work," and the wall was finished in fifty-two days.

How is this story like the story about the building of the Tabernacle that Gramps told Sara and Jeff?

How is it like Gramps' story about Jethro and Moses?

Explain in your own words what "The people had a mind to work" means to you?

Do you think that Sara had a mind to work? Did Jeff? Michael? Marsha?

How is the heart connected with the will to work?

What does the sentence, "It matters not whether a man does little or much as long as he directs his heart to God," mean to you?

What can Jeff and Sara learn from this advice?

What can you learn?

How can Jethro's advice to Moses work for you? At home? At school? At play? With other people?

Can you remember a time when you did a piece of work with your whole heart?

How did it turn out? How did you feel about the result?

2. Another story in the Midrash tells us that Jethro met Moses for the first time in the desert of Midian. When Moses decided to be a shepherd for Jethro's flocks, Jethro warned him, "In Egypt you were a great prince and here you will be just a humble shepherd." Moses answered, "It matters not to me—no one should despise work done by any man!"

Do you think these words came from Moses' heart? How do you know?

Can you prove that the Rabbis of the Talmud agreed with Moses?

Have you ever heard people you know make fun of their neighbor's work? What would Moses have said to them? What did you say? Why?

3. A Chasidic Rabbi was once asked, "How can a man know if he is really sorry after he has done an evil deed?" The Rabbi answered, "If he loses the desire to do the evil deed again."

   Do you think Jeff was truly sorry for what he had done? How did he have to prove it?

   Was Sara sorry for the bad deed she had committed or was she sorry for herself? How do you know?

   Would Beruriah have agreed with what the Chasidic Rabbi said?

   How do you feel when your sins are forgiven?

4. In Ethics of the Fathers we read, "Be not like servants who serve their master for the sake of receiving a reward. Be rather like servants who serve their masters without thinking of a reward."

   What does this sentence mean to you?

   Do you think Jeff worse because he caused Joshua to get hurt or because he left his work undone? Do you think Jeff would have been so upset if Joshua hadn't been hurt?

   Is there anything wrong with expecting a reward when you do something for anyone? Did the Rabbis mean that we must not take rewards when we receive them?

   Do your parents give you rewards when you help at home? When you get good grades at school? When you do a good deed?

   Would you do the same things if you didn't get a reward? Why?

5. Hillel also said, "If not now, when?"

   Do you think Jeff intended to let Michael and Steven do his work?

   Was he just putting off the work till later?

   What can happen when you don't feel like doing the work given to you to do?

Can you think of a time when delaying your work harmed you or someone you know?

What did you learn from this experience?

6. In school Jeff received his best mark in science. It was his favorite subject and nothing was too hard for him when it came to science. He didn't like history and paid little attention to it. One day he brought home a report with a failure in history. His father knew that Jeff wanted a telescope with all his heart and promised to buy Jeff one if he raised his history mark to an "A." Jeff thought this was a wonderful deal and worked as hard as he could for the next few months. Every spare minute was spent with his history until he knew it backwards and forwards. The thought of the telescope spurred him on. His work had results. Soon his average in history climbed.

Just a few days before the report cards were due to come out, the history teacher announced that a final test would determine the mark on the card. On the day before the test Jeff just happened to be mimeographing some science outlines for the science teacher. One of the outlines slipped under the machine. When Jeff dug it out, to his great surprise he found the history test for the next day. Evidently the teacher had missed the test when it slipped under the machine.

Here was Jeff's chance to get an "A" and a telescope!

What do you think Jeff did? Remember he had studied his history for two months and he knew it cold!

Write the ending to this story as you think it would end.

Do you think Jeff's father should have bribed him with a telescope?

If Jeff did get the "A" and the telescope, do you think he stopped studying his history after that? Why?

Dramatize the scene in the mimeograph room. Choose five children to be the actors. Have them pretend they are Jeff, Michael, Steven, Joshua, and Ben. Say what you think each child would do and say when he finds the test. Choose two girls to be Sara and Marsha. Let them dramatize how they would feel and what they would do.

7. A MOONLIGHT HIKE

At ten o'clock Bill and the boys left the cabin. Past Universal Lawn, past the Thinking Place, they walked until they came to the woods. Excitement shone on their faces.

It was Jeff who had thought of a moonlight hike. "I read a story once," he said one night, "where some boys decided to explore the woods when the moon was full. All kinds of animals appeared and did all sorts of wonderful things. Wouldn't it be exciting if our bunk could have an adventure like that?"

"Jiminy cricket!" said Joshua, "what a treat that would be!"

The eager glow on Joshua's face helped Bill to decide. He asked Aaron if Emes could go on a hike the next time the moon was full. At first Aaron had objected because of the late hour but when Bill had promised that the boys would snatch some extra sleep during the afternoon, Aaron had given permission.

And now the time had arrived.

A great, round moon sailed through the sky, flooding the path before them with silver. Stillness wrapped the entrance to the woods. The whole world seemed to be holding its breath waiting for something to happen.

Just before they entered, Bill called a halt. "Now, remember," he warned, "if you make loud sounds the animals won't show. Try to talk in whispers and walk as softly as you can."

Bill said to Joshua, "I'll walk close to you and try to describe everything we see. Whatever I leave out, the boys will add—in whispers."

At that moment Joshua felt a wet tongue licking his free hand. He knew immediately that Lovon had joined the hike. With a laugh Joshua twined his fingers in Lovon's collar. "Look Bill, Lovon wants to come, too."

Everyone laughed when Lovon's tail wagged his agreement. His ears stood up like tents and he gave a short happy bark.

Joshua's hand tightened on Lovon's collar and he looked at Bill, "Lovon can be my seeing-eye dog and lead me. Please, Bill, let him come."

Bill smiled. "All right, Josh. Maybe Lovon will lead us to some interesting places. He knows every corner of these woods." Bill patted Lovon with a warning, "Now, don't you go scaring the animals with your yelps." Lovon cocked his head at the boys as if he understood.

Into the woods they walked. On both sides of the silver path were dark shadows. "Keep to the lighted path," said Bill as a last warning.

All at once the woods sprang alive.

Across the road marched a family of skunks on a moonlight outing. Slowly, the mother waddled along, her seven babies following, strung out in Indian file. Her plume of a tail rose in the air like a proud flag. Two of the babies closest to her decided to have some fun. Rolling over on their backs they pawed playfully at each other. But Mrs. Skunk was in no mood for such nonsense. With a quick about-face, she cuffed them on their little heads, scolding them with fast skunk talk.

The boys watched quietly. Lovon barked, straining to get away from Joshua. Michael bent down to Lovon's ear and whispered, "Quiet, Lovon. Do you want to get us sprayed? When a

skunk's tail is up in the air like that you have to *watch out*."
Lovon did as he was told.

"They're certainly taking their own good time crossing that road," whispered Steve to Jeff.

"Why should they hurry?" laughed Jeff, softly. "They have plenty of ammunition to fire at anybody who's dumb enough to get in their way."

They watched Mrs. Skunk flip a stone over in her path. As each baby came to the stone, it copied the mother exactly. But when the last skunk turned the stone a surprise greeted it. Out hopped a fat toad. The baby skunk waddled after the toad. But the toad was faster. It hopped away into the bushes before the skunk could catch up with it. When the skunk turned around again its family had melted into the darkness. Whimpering sadly, the skunk stood outside the shadows, its scared eyes darting in all directions.

"Poor baby," said Ben, "it doesn't know what to do." With a leap, he rushed to the rescue. Picking up the skunk with a gentle hand, he entered the bushes where they had last seen the skunk family. Inside, he placed the baby on the mossy ground. With a quick shove he directed it toward the place where he could see the mother's tail gleaming in the darkness. "Get going, skunklet!" he ordered. "Follow your mother."

Racing back to the path he found the boys and Bill waiting.

Steven sniffed noisily, walking around Ben in a circle. Ben laughed. "Not this time, my friend. I still smell like myself."

"*End of adventure number one!*" said Joshua, holding up one finger.

"Kee Tov!" added Bill.

Above them the moon bumped into a passing cloud and disappeared inside. Now the pathway filled with strange shadows. The boys turned on their flashlights and followed the streams of light.

Into the light glided a raccoon, its barber-pole tail spread behind it. It was pushing an egg along the ground with its nose.

In the middle of the path it stopped and sat up on its haunches. Clutching the egg in two front paws it nipped a hole in the shell and began to sip daintily. It closed its eyes with delight.

Joshua felt Lovon tugging at his collar. With a hard pull, Lovon broke loose. His ears twitched forward and with a growl he sprang into action. Planking himself in front of the raccoon he grabbed the egg with his mouth. But Lovon was careless. Before he could get a firm grip, the egg dropped to the ground, shattering its shell. He watched the yolk trickle out in a yellow stream. Out slid his fast tongue to lap up the yolk. But the raccoon wasn't in a generous mood. With an angry "gerr" it slapped a paw on Lovon's nose. This was too great an insult for Lovon. Bracing himself, he prepared to defend his dog honor.

Before the boys could do anything about it, a noisy whirl of raccoon and dog rolled on the ground. Over and over they tumbled. The boys couldn't tell which was dog and which was raccoon. Bill was just about to separate them when Lovon decided to quit. Picking a fight with a tough raccoon was getting him nowhere fast. He had met his match and he knew it.

With a jerk he freed himself and leaped away yelping. The raccoon decided that it had had enough, too. Whickering softly to itself, it backed away into the bushes. The last thing the boys saw were the white stripes on its black face.

"The raccoon's face looks like a clown mask," giggled Michael to Joshua.

Lovon trotted back to the boys, his ears drooping and his tail tucked between his legs. Michael laughed. Leaping on Michael's chest Lovon put both paws around him, begging for sympathy.

"*End of adventure number two!*" said Joshua, holding up two fingers.

"Kee Tov!" added all the boys.

The moon slid out of its hiding-place and cast its silver on the path once more. A new road appeared on the left. They decided to investigate.

A white glow in the darkness attracted Jeff's attention. He bent to examine it. To his surprise he discovered a flower that looked like a white pipe. He called to the group and pointed to the velvety petals resting on a bed of decayed leaves.

"How can a lovely flower like that grow in such an ugly place?" asked Jeff, looking up at Bill.

Jeff's question stumped Bill. "I don't really know, Jeff," he said, with a thoughtful expression. "Perhaps the decayed leaves put something into the soil the white pipe needs to grow. What I do know, however, is that everything God created has a purpose, even though we can't always understand it."

They continued down the path. All at once they came to a pool gleaming in the moonlight. Clouds of bright moths zoomed after fireflies winking their lanterns on and off. Jeff pointed to a brown bat zigging its way over the pool, its baby clinging to its body. The beauty before them filled them with quiet joy.

Bill pointed to a long log near the edge of the pool. They knelt behind it silently waiting for something to happen. They were very quiet. Bill held Lovon in his arms to be sure he would be quiet, too.

They didn't have long to wait.

Suddenly, Jeff pointed to the far side of the water. They saw a deer peep out of the bushes. It edged out slowly, peering to the left and right. With a wide swish of its white tail the deer stopped and waited. A tiny spotted baby tottered out after its mother.

Bill described the scene in a whisper to Joshua, adding, "She uses her white tail as a warning signal."

Mother and child stood motionless at the water's edge and dipped their graceful heads to drink. At that instant Ben stood up to get a better look. He toppled over the log with a yell that ripped the moonlit stillness.

He clapped his hands over his mouth but it was too late. The mother deer lifted a startled head. Stamping her hoofs frantically, she flashed a tail warning to her baby. With long leaps they took flight, bounding away into the bushes.

Ben was full of apologies. "How clumsy can I get?" he scolded himself in disgust. "Someone ought to poke me in the nose. I deserve it!" Bill ruffled Ben's hair. "Don't feel so terrible, Ben. What we saw was pretty wonderful. The deer would probably have caught our scent anyway." Michael slapped Ben on the back and grinned, "Too bad you didn't have your trusty camera. You looked mighty silly sprawled over that log!"

Ben felt better. "Too bad my camera can't take colored pictures. What a collection of shots I'd have by now."

"*End of adventure number three!*" said Joshua, holding up three fingers.

"Kee Tov!" shouted the boys, forgetting to talk softly.

Near the water's edge Steven accidentally stepped on a turtle's tail. He jumped aside and saw the round head disappear into its shell house. In popped the tail, the head, and the legs. In a wink all its doors were shut tightly and it lay motionless. Steven flipped the turtle over on its back and examined every inch of it. It acted as if it were dead.

He called to the boys and Bill. Jeff remembered something he had read in a science book. Quickly, he turned the turtle over, saying, "If we leave the turtle on its back, it'll die."

What followed made the boys roar. Out sprang the four legs, the head and the tail, as if Jeff had pressed a magic button. Without a backward glance the turtle scrambled off into the pool.

"How can it carry that heavy shell without getting tired?" asked Steven.

Bill replied, "The Rabbis in the Talmud said that God decided on each part of the body and set each part in its proper place. The turtle needs its shell for protection. You saw that just now. Perhaps the turtle doesn't think its shell is so heavy."

"*End of adventure number four!*" said Joshua, holding up four fingers.

"Kee Tov!" added the boys.

Just at that moment they heard an S.O.S. of excited yelps. They scooted toward the sound. It didn't take long to discover that Lovon was in trouble. And what trouble!

Lovon, barking furiously, stood close—much too close—to a porcupine busily chipping away at the bark of a tree. The boys held their breath as they watched the porcupine back away from the tree toward Lovon.

"Run, Lovon! Run for your life!" shouted Ben, jumping up and down like a jack-in-the-box.

But it was too late! The porcupine's quills were standing upright on its pin-cushion tail. The boys covered their eyes when they saw the prickly tail attack. With a wild yelp, Lovon toppled over, his legs pawing the air.

With a satisfied grunt the porcupine turned back to the bark as if nothing had happened. The boys had to laugh. The quills sticking out in all directions made Lovon look as if he were wired for sound. But Lovon didn't think it was funny! He streaked down the path like a guided missile. When he was sure a safe distance separated him and his attacker, he fell down with a tired plop.

The boys scrambled after him.

Ben pulled a quill out of Lovon's nose. "Now will you stick your nose into porcupine business?" he asked, stroking the dog's back.

Steven pulled a quill out of Lovon's ear. "Tangling with a porcupine is dangerous business," he said, patting Lovon's head.

Everyone took turns tugging. With each pull, Lovon whimpered. When his face was free of quills, Jeff gathered some damp leaves nearby. He piled them on Lovon to cool his hot face. Lovon stuck his tongue out of the leaves to lick Jeff's kind hands.

"*End of adventure number five!*" said Joshua, holding up his whole hand.

"Not so Kee Tov!" said the boys, laughing at Lovon.

Lovon cocked his head and barked. "Enough is enough!" the bark seemed to mean. And before the boys could stop him, he streaked down the path toward camp.

A patch of mushrooms caught Michael's eye. He bent to look closer and blinked. What he saw was almost unbelievable. Under a mushroom umbrella sat a deer-mouse, its long tail curled around the stem like a pretzel. It gazed at Michael, too frightened to move. The seamlike line near its mouth trembled. Michael flashed a friendly smile. "Don't worry, little deer-mouse," he said softly, "I won't harm you." Michael backed away slowly. When he told the boys and Bill what he had seen, they rushed to look. But the little deer-mouse had found the courage to scamper away.

From beyond a nearby hedge came a steady drumming. Swiftly they ran to investigate. Through the hedge they peered out into a clearing of tall grass. What they saw made them freeze to attention.

The air was full of rabbits shooting up into the moonlight.

"It's a rabbit dance!" whispered Bill to Joshua, who was begging to be told what was happening. "I'll tell you about it later. I can't talk now."

The powerful hind legs of the rabbits seemed to be dancing to the music of an invisible orchestra. Every leap seemed to be part of the dance. Up in the air they soared bumping into each other, and tumbling swiftly to the ground. No sooner did they hit the earth, when up again they bounced, twirling their bodies into somersaults over each other.

Their speechless audience didn't know where to look first. So much was going on at one time!

All at once a woodpecker poked its red head out of its apartment house tree and trilled a gay song. As if a signal had been given for the music to stop, the dance ended. One by one the rabbits hopped away and vanished into the woods leaving the clearing silent in the moonlight.

The boys let out their breath with a loud whoosh.

Everyone talked at once, describing the miracle to Joshua.

"I can see exactly what happened," said Joshua, his face glowing. "Maybe the rabbits did hear music," he chuckled. "We'll never know. After all, we're not rabbits."

"You may be right, Joshua," laughed Bill, looking at his watch.

"*End of adventure number six!*" said Joshua, holding up six fingers.

"Kee Tov!" added the boys.

"Time to get back to camp," said Bill.

The boys groaned. "Do we have to go back?" asked Michael. "I was wishing the night would never end!"

"Get going!" laughed Bill, pushing Michael toward the road. "Besides, you all need your beauty rest."

They came out of the woods and walked through the pasture skirting the Big House. And here they bumped into the best adventure of all. They gazed in wide-eyed wonder.

A brand new calf swayed on spindly legs close to its mother. The mother was giving the calf its first bath. With loving swishes, her tongue lapped across the back and neck, and along the sides. Not a part of the calf was left unwashed. After the bath, the mother gently nuzzled the calf on the ear, giving her baby its first kiss. The boys could hear the murmur of cow talk between them.

And then to their complete joy, the calf tottered on wobbly legs around to the mother's side and searched until it found the udder where it could drink.

"In wisdom hast Thou made us all," said Bill. "The whole earth is full of Thy creatures."

"*Adventure number seven!*" said Joshua, in a whisper.

"Kee Tov!" added the boys, softly.

"And the best Kee Tov of all!" added Michael, the wonder still in his voice.

WHAT DO YOU THINK?

1. The Rabbis in the Midrash tell us that when God created the animals He said to them, "Cooperate with Me in forming man. Each of you will give to man one of your very best qualities. In this way man will not only be like you, but he will represent the finest qualities that you have."

   And so the ant gave honesty, the lion courage, the eagle industriousness, the cat modesty, and the dove gentleness.

   Think of all the Kee Tov adventures the boys had on the moonlight hike. How can these adventures teach us about what the Rabbis call Tzar Ba-ale Chayim, *"The pain of living things," which is the reason for showing mercy toward all creatures?*

   Can you observe Tzar-Ba-ale Chayim in your homes? With your friends? Towards your pets?

2. The Talmud tells a story about two dogs who guarded a flock of sheep. Each day they quarreled fiercely. One day a hungry wolf attacked one of the dogs. The other dog thought to himself, "If I do not help my neighbor today, the wolf will no doubt attack me tomorrow." Thereupon the two dogs settled their quarrel and decided to work together in peace. Together they killed the wolf.

   How did the two dogs in the story help each other in the end?

   What adventure in the story seems to say the same thing as the Talmud story?

   Can you think of an instance when you wasted time quarreling with a friend? How did the quarrel affect what you were doing?

   Do you find it difficult to forgive your friend after a quarrel?

   Do you wait for your friend to settle the quarrel or are you the first to try to make peace?

Why is the advice in the Talmud, "Great is peace and hateful is quarreling" good advice to follow?

3. Steven wondered why the turtle had to carry such a heavy house around with it wherever it traveled. What did Bill tell him? In the Midrash we are told that King David once doubted God's wisdom in creating the spider. "O God," said King David, "how useless is the spider. It can only spin a web without value. It spins all the year, yet its web cannot be made into a robe." God replied to King David, saying, "Do not speak ill of the things I have created. A day will come when you will be saved by them. Then you will know that I have a purpose for everything on earth."

   Later David learned that even a spider had a reason for being in the world. Once when he was fleeing from King Saul and his soldiers, he hid in a cave. Across the opening of the cave a spider spun a web while King David was inside. King Saul and his men came to the cave. When the soldiers saw the web they decided that no one could be in the cave because the web was untouched. And so David's life was saved because of the spider he thought was useless.

What did Bill say to Steven about the turtle's house that is like what God said to King David?

Think of some insects and animals that are helpful to man. In what special way are they created to help man?

What did Bill say at the end of the story that says the same thing?

How did the sights the boys saw make them feel there ·was a God who created the world and who keeps it going?

What sights have you seen that make you feel the same way?

4. Do you remember when Michael saw the seamlike line next to the mouth of the white-footed mouse tremble?

   The Midrash has a wonderful legend about how the rabbis tried to explain this.

It happened when all the animals were in Noah's Ark during the time of the Flood. A mouse was sitting next to a cat. Suddenly, the cat jumped on the mouse for no good reason at all. The mouse ran into a hole nearby to protect itself. The cat followed but it was too late. It thrust its paw into the hole. The mouse opened its mouth hoping to bite the cat's paw. But its mouth wasn't wide enough. The cat's paw clawed and ripped the mouse's cheek.

After the bitter fight the mouse came to Noah and said, "O good Noah, please sew up my cheek. My enemy, the cat, has torn it." Quickly, Noah pulled a hair from the tail of a pig and repaired the damage. That is why the mouse has a seamlike line next to the mouth to this very day.

What did the boys do on the hike that showed lovingkindness like Noah?

5. Bill told this Talmud story to the boys when they returned from the hike:

In a small town in Palestine there lived a wicked innkeeper. It was his custom to persuade his guests to rise and dress just before daylight, and to leave the inn with him. The innkeeper insisted on accompanying his guests for part of the way. "This is the best way to travel," he would tell them. "Now you will not have to journey during the great heat of the day." Once they were on their way, the innkeeper would guide his guests to a cave where a band of crooks was waiting to attack the guests and rob them of all their possessions. Later the thieves would divide the loot between themselves and the innkeeper.

One evening Rabbi Meir stopped at the inn. When the innkeeper saw his sleek donkey and the valuable cargo it carried, he wanted it for himself. Just before sunrise he awoke Rabbi Meir and tried to persuade him to leave the inn. But the rabbi refused to go. "I am waiting for my brother, Kee Tov. He is planning to meet me here in the morning," he said.

The innkeeper kept a sharp eye out for the rabbi's brother but Kee Tov didn't arrive. In the morning Rabbi Meir prepared to leave.

"Where is your brother, Kee Tov?" the innkeeper asked the rabbi.

The rabbi smiled gently. "My brother, Kee Tov, is the daylight. It is written in the Bible, 'And God saw the light. Kee Tov—it is good.'"

Why did the boys say, "Kee Tov" after each adventure?

Were their reasons for saying "Kee Tov" like Rabbi Meir's?

How were they different?

Can you find a way in which they are alike?

Can Kee Tov mean different things to different people? How?

What does Kee Tov say to you? At home? At school? At play? In your neighborhood?

8. S'GOOLO SAYS THANKS

Tamar sat on a log waiting for Harold, the head swimming counselor, to give her a swimming lesson. Beyond the crib she could see Marsha and Sara practicing their backstroke. Susan and Ann were helping each other improve their crawl. Tamar sighed. Her bunkmates were ready for the raft test and she was still in the crib trying to learn to swim. Why was she so slow? She was trying so hard. But it was no use! She was too scared of the water!

Far out on the lake Tamar could see a sailboat with two Giborim girls at the tiller. A sudden breeze caught the sail and billowed it into a great white arc. She'd never swim well enough to handle a sailboat like that. She just knew it!

Tamar saw Harold stop on the center dock and blow his whistle twice, the signal for each pair of buddies to join hands and lift them high in the air. The counselors, scattered over the docks, counted the raised hands. Tamar knew how safe the water was at Kee Tov, yet as Harold came toward her, the old panicky feeling began in the pit of her stomach and climbed into her throat.

She looked with envy at the bobbing red caps of her bunk-mates in the sunlit water. She could hear them joking and laughing. Even Sara forgot to be unhappy in the water. To everyone's surprise Sara had turned out to be the best swimmer in the bunk. Tamar wished Sara would help her, but she was afraid to ask. You never knew how Sara was going to act. Most of the time she was so cross.

"Are you ready, Tamar?" asked Harold, pulling her up with a strong hand. Tamar nodded shyly. Hand in hand they walked into the water. Harold could feel Tamar trembling beside him. Into the deeper water they waded.

"I'll never learn. I just know it," said Tamar, holding onto his hand tightly.

Harold loosened her hand gently and began to teach her the crawl. Tamar's eyes didn't leave him for a minute.

Harold tried to give Tamar the confidence she needed. "Do you know, Tamar, you've quite a good stroke there. Think about your breathing. You can be a champ if you'll just believe in yourself. You have to remember that in the water you're a fish with a tail." Tamar smiled gratefully at Harold. When he talked like that, she felt as brave as a lion. She began to work harder.

After the lesson Tamar ran along the dock toward the girls. She bent over the water to call to Marsha who was swimming a short distance away. At that moment, Miriam hoisted herself out of the water and backed onto the runway—straight into Tamar. Tamar was caught off balance and hit the water like a hammer. Down she plunged to the bottom. In a second she bobbed up, her hands waving with terror. Down she went again. The girls of S'goolo watched, frozen with fear.

In that instant Miriam dived. The girls found their voices and screamed. Harold came running at top speed. The seconds seemed like hours before Miriam surfaced, holding Tamar's head above the water.

Quickly, they placed Tamar on the dock face down, turning

her head to the side. She was like a statue, motionless, her eyes closed. The girls anxiously surrounded her. Marsha drew a frightened breath.

Harold took command. He'd have to give first aid. There wasn't a second to lose. Kneeling down facing her head, he placed the palms of his hands on Tamar's back, just below the shoulders. Rocking forward, he pressed slowly, counting to himself. And then rocking backward he lifted his hands, still counting. Again and again he repeated the motions with a steady rhythm. Press—let go! Press—let go! He felt a hot tear on his hand and looked up to see Marsha crying.

All at once Susan burst out, "O God, please save Tamar. Don't let her die! I'll do anything in the world for You—anything. You have to save her!"

Marsha gazed at Tamar with brimming eyes. Deep in her heart she prayed, "O God, please help Harold save Tamar." Gathering courage from her prayer, Marsha kneeled and whispered to Tamar, "Don't be afraid, Tamar. Harold will save you. He knows what to do."

And then, as if Marsha's voice had awakened her, Tamar stirred. She opened her eyes slowly and lifted her head. The fear she saw in everyone's eyes told her immediately how worried they were. A tiny smile appeared on her lips. "I'm all right now," she said. "Don't worry." Her voice was so low they had to strain to hear.

The tightness in Marsha's throat disappeared, and was replaced by a thankfulness. She smiled at Harold, "You knew just what to do. I'm glad you were here."

Harold wiped the water from his face. Tamar said, "Thanks for saving me, Harold. If I knew how to swim I wouldn't have been so much trouble to you." Her words of thanks came from deep within her.

Harold grinned. "You know how to swim, Tamar. You just forgot to be a fish with a tail. Remember?"

Marsha recalled the dive Miriam had made after Tamar.

"Miriam saved you, too, Tamar. And was she fast! All *we* could do was scream." Marsha flashed an admiring glance at Miriam.

"I'll be sure to look behind me after this," came Miriam's quick reply. She helped Tamar to her feet.

Tamar gave Miriam a tight hug. "I'll never forget what you did for me. Thanks, Miriam."

All the girls crowded around Tamar.

"Were you scared?" asked Susan.

The girls giggled when Tamar wrinkled her nose at the lake. "That whole lake poured into my stomach, I think," she said.

Three blasts from Harold's whistle and swimming period was over.

Marsha stopped on the beach to thank God for helping Harold to save Tamar. Her grateful prayer came straight from her heart.

*   *   *

At six o'clock the girls walked to the chapel for the Sabbath services. Everyone was scrubbed clean and shining in honor of the Sabbath. The girls in S'goolo sang a marching song as they swung along the path. All at once Miriam noticed that Sara was missing. Immediately she knew the reason. In the cabin Sara had raised a fuss, refusing to wear her special Sabbath clothing. It had taken a long time before Miriam had been able to convince her to put on a white skirt and blouse. Miriam sighed. She had tried in every way she knew to help Sara. What was she going to do?

"Marsha, will you please run back to the bunk and see if Sara is there," she said.

"May I go with Marsha?" asked Tamar.

"Yes—and hurry. Or you'll miss the services."

But Sara was not in the cabin. "Maybe she's at the beach," suggested Tamar.

They found Sara sitting in a sailboat tied to the dock.

"Come on, Sara," urged Marsha, "you'll miss the services."

"Nobody cares the least bit whether I go or not!" Sara lifted her eyes to the sail above her. How she wished she were sailing away from Kee Tov—far, far away.

Marsha decided to take matters in her own hands. She was going to tell Sara what she thought of her once and for all! "We can't go back without you. Gosh, Sara, Miriam tries so hard to please you, even when you don't deserve it. If you ask me, she's too kind. You're just plain mean!"

Sara glanced away from the sail. Marsha and Tamar saw tears were rolling down her cheeks. Her unhappiness reached out and pierced their hearts like a thorn.

"Nobody likes me. Nobody at all! Everything I do is wrong!"

"Why do you think we don't like you?" asked Marsha, suddenly.

"See! You *don't* like me! You just said so!" Sara twisted the question around making Marsha uncomfortable.

"But Sara, you did say that everything you do is wrong. You just said that, didn't you?" Marsha tried to make Sara face her problem. "Can't you change the wrong into right?"

"I could try," Sara hesitated. It was hard for her to get the words out right. "I could try to make you like me, but I don't know how!" She flung her hand out helplessly towards Marsha and Tamar. A strange feeling was growing inside her. Suddenly, she knew she wanted their friendship. "I'm always so grumpy and I raise a fuss every time I don't get my way," she admitted. "I'm a hopeless case!"

Marsha looked at Tamar but she had nothing to say. The three girls were quiet. The problem rose like a high wall they couldn't climb. "Look," said Marsha, finally, "I've thought of a way to keep you from getting cross when you don't get your way."

Sara lifted her eyes to Marsha hopefully.

"Every time we see the '*I won't do it*' expression on your face, we'll shout, 'H.M.!' and then you'll stop to think—and—you won't get mad! It's as easy as that!" Marsha jumbled the words together and grinned.

Sara and Tamar had big questions in their eyes. Marsha was talking in riddles. What was she driving at?

"H.M.? What in the world does that mean?" asked Sara.

"H. means 'help' and M. means 'me.' *Help me!*" explained Marsha, chuckling when she saw the puzzled looks change to understanding.

"I get it," said Sara. "*Help me!*" She thought about it for a few seconds. Could Marsha's advice really help? She looked at the girls—wondering.

"But Sara," continued Marsha, earnestly, "if you want us to like you, you have to try to like *us*."

"Gramps says that, too," Sara recalled. For the first time she knew in her heart that Marsha and Tamar really wanted to help her. The icicles in her chest began to melt. The warm smiles of the girls hinted that the friendless days at Kee Tov were at last over. She felt as if she had been given another chance.

Tamar had another suggestion. "I know another way," she laughed. "Think of swimming when you want to make a fuss. You're happy when you're in the water. Would that help?"

They all burst into giggles.

And then Sara looked at Tamar and snapped her fingers. "I know what I'm going to do. I'm going to help you pass your crib test. I just know I can."

Tamar's face lit up like a hundred candles.

Marsha looked admiringly at the new Sara.

"Let's hurry," she said, "we'll miss the Sabbath Queen."

Laughing gaily, they sped along the path, arm in arm.

In the chapel Michael gazed at the wide window behind the altar. On it was a huge figure of Moses made of mosaic, bits of colored glass. Above Moses were the two Tablets of the Law. A *Ner Tomid* of twisted black iron held a light that burned brightly before the Tablets. In front of the Ark was a high table with two brass candlesticks waiting to be kindled. Gramps and Bill and two older boys waited near the Ark.

Michael saw the wide doors to the balcony open. Joshua

lifted his violin and drew the bow across the strings. The lovely melody of "L'cho Dodi" filled the chapel and the choir began to sing. Slowly through the door danced the Sabbath Queen, her long white robe floating gracefully. Adorning her black hair was a wreath of white flowers. Behind her, in long blue robes, danced her handmaidens. On their heads they wore blue flowers laced with shiny leaves. Down the flagstone stairs to every part of the chapel they danced. They came to a halt before the Ark.

When the music stopped, the Sabbath Queen kindled the Sabbath lights. *Boruch ato adonoi elohenu melech ho-olom asher kid'shonu b'mitzvosov v'tzivonu l'hadlik ner shel Shabos.* The lovely old chant floated through the air.

Later, Michael looked up from his service booklet toward Marsha's section of the balcony. She wasn't there. He stretched his neck searching for her. Miriam caught his eye and saw the question there. She went over to Aaron, whispered something into his ear, and left the chapel. What had happened to Marsha? Was she sick? Worry raced down Michael's spine.

Miriam hurried across Universal Lawn. Near the Big House she sighed with relief. Running toward her were the girls.

"Are we late?" asked Tamar, knowing they were.

"Did we miss the dance of the Sabbath Queen?" asked Marsha, hoping they hadn't.

Sara took all the blame. "It was my fault, Miriam," she explained, "and I promise I won't cause any trouble again." Her eyes begged Miriam's forgiveness.

Miriam tried not to show her surprise. She hustled them into the chapel. "It's all right. I was a little worried. Tell me about it later." To Sara she whispered, "Of course I forgive you." When she saw the happiness on Sara's face she squeezed her hand. "Welcome to Kee Tov, dear."

They were just in time to hear Bill's sermon. "Tonight we are gathered together to thank God for His daily blessings. Long ago the Jews sacrificed animals to God. But the prophets

taught that God didn't want these sacrifices. God, they said, wanted justice, mercy, truth, and lovingkindness. How can we show our love for God? By the righteous deeds we do for each other. One of our great teachers put it this way, 'If someone comes to you and asks for help, you must act as though there were no one else in the world to help that person but yourself.' "

Sara smiled at Marsha and Tamar, including Ann and Susan in the smile, too. In her heart she knew they had done just that. Her whole being felt as if it would burst with thankfulness. She had friends, now. And she meant to keep them. She knew how lonely it was without friends.

"And now," said Bill, "I have a true story for you, straight out of the pages of Jewish history." Bill twinkled at the campers. "In Russia long ago, there lived a wonderful rabbi, Rabbi Israel Salanter. Once, on Yom Kippur Eve, they say, his synagogue was crowded with people waiting for the *Kol Nidrei* service to begin. They waited and waited for their beloved rabbi to appear. After a long while they became alarmed. Messengers were sent to search for him but they returned without him. The Yom Kippur services had to be held without the rabbi. Finally he arrived. Can you imagine the joy with which he was greeted? But when the people heard the reason for his absence their joy turned to astonishment. On the way to the synagogue the rabbi told them, he had passed a house where a baby was crying. Inside he found an infant, screaming with fright. Rabbi Salanter understood at once that the mother must have gone to the synagogue, believing her child was fast asleep. Picking up the baby he cradled it in his arms and watched over it until it went back to sleep. One of the men said, 'But Rabbi, this is the holiest day of the year. Now you are too late to say the prayer asking God to forgive you.' The rabbi smiled gently. 'When a man helps another who is in trouble, his deed is also a prayer.' "

Outside, after the services, Miriam gathered the girls around her. Ann, Susan, and Miriam listened while Sara, Marsha, and Tamar talked. Lovon scampered out of the Thinking Place and pushed himself into the middle of the conversation. He found himself near Sara and drew away quickly. Sara bent down and stroked his back. "I'm sorry, Lovon. I've been mean to you— and I promise to change."

Lovon wagged his tail happily and licked her hand.

Miriam thought of something she wanted to do. "It's time to gather around the flagpole," she told the girls. "You walk up there now and I'll join you in a while. I want to talk to Aaron."

At the flagpole, the campers buzzed with excitement. Who would get a Torah award tonight? A cheer arose when they saw Miriam, Aaron, and Gramps approaching.

Aaron began to talk. "Kee Tov is proud to award three Torahs tonight and this is a good time to give them to you." Aaron dangled the Torah and smiled at Gramps. A groan came from the campers. "Who? Who?" they shouted.

Aaron told them. "To the Giborim bunk, *Libenu*, for mercy. During one of their ball games they discovered a bird sitting on its eggs near third base on the ball field. Rather than disturb the eggs, the boys built a tall screen to protect the eggs when they played. The Bible says that, 'if you happen to come upon a bird's nest on the ground with eggs, you shall not take away the mother bird with her young.' Like their name, 'our heart,' Libenu had a heart for God's creatures.

"To the Na-arim bunk, *N'vi-im*, for lovingkindness. On their overnight hike one of their group slipped and twisted his ankle. It swelled and he couldn't walk. The N'vi-im built a cot of sticks and vines and carried their bunkmate back to camp in record time to get a doctor's attention. The Bible says, 'Love thy neighbor as thyself,' to N'vi-im, the prophets, for lovingkindness."

"To the Y'lodim bunk, S'goolo, for lovingkindness, too," announced Aaron, smiling in the direction of the girls. "Loving your neighbor as yourself is God's most important commandment. The girls in S'goolo have learned to help each other live in love and peace. To S'goolo—for lovingkindness."

Sara flushed to the roots of her hair. Aaron was talking about her—and the trouble she had caused. Her eyes sparked in the old way and she turned to the girls, about to explode angrily. "H.M.," whispered her bunkmates, together.

The angry spark sputtered out like a spent candle and Sara laughed instead. "You win!" she laughed.

"No, *you* win!" said Miriam. It was hard to tell who was shining more, Sara or the Torah. She grinned at Gramps whose delighted smile told her *she* had really won.

WHAT DO YOU THINK?

1. Later that evening Marsha said to Miriam, "I feel terrible because I missed the service in the chapel. I love to pray." Miriam replied, "But, Marsha, remember Bill's story. A good deed can be a prayer, too, in action."

   When do you think Marsha and Tamar's conversation at the beach with Sara became a prayer?

   Look at it the other way around. How do prayers we say in the temple lead to good deeds?

2. In the Book of Proverbs in the Bible, we are told, "Withhold not help from the needy when it is in your power to give it."

   Can you think of a command in the Bible that says the same thing in another way?

   How did Marsha and Tamar obey this commandment? Harold? The N'vi-im?

   Forgiveness must be included in the mitzvah, "Love your neighbor as yourself."

   How did Miriam obey this mitzvah? Tamar and Marsha?

Do you like the way Marsha and Tamar solved Sara's problem? Why?

Can you think of a better solution that might have helped Sara?

Dramatize the conversation using the best ideas.

Do you think that Gramps helped Sara before the girls tried? How?

Has anyone helped you the way the girls helped Sara? Tell us about it.

3. In the story both Marsha and Susan prayed for Tamar.

   What did Marsha say? Susan?

   Which prayer was a demand?

   Which prayer did you like best? Why?

   How did Marsha's prayer help her? How did it help Tamar?

   Whose prayer seemed to say, "God, if You will do something for me, I'll do something for You"?

   What's wrong with that kind of a prayer?

   When you want something very badly, should you pray to God to give it to you? What does it mean when we ask God "to give" something to us? What happens if you don't get it? Is that always bad? Is it God's fault? Whose fault is it? What is the most grown-up kind of prayer?

4. In Psalm 104 the Psalmist says:

I WILL SING UNTO THE LORD AS LONG AS I LIVE,
I WILL SING PRAISE TO MY GOD WHILE I HAVE MY
   BEING.

   Why is the Psalmist grateful to God?

   What else beside gratitude does God want from us?

   How is observing God's commandments a form of gratitude?

How did the Sabbath Queen's dance show gratitude to God?

How did Marsha show her gratitude to God when Tamar was safe again?

What other prayers do you know that say thanks to God?

The Talmud says, "No matter how small the kindness, one should always feel gratefulness and express the feeling."

How did Marsha express her thankfulness to Miriam? To Harold?

How did Sara? Tamar? Bill? The campers at Kee Tov?

List some of the ways we express gratitude at home. At school. With our friends.

When someone shows you thankfulness, how do you feel?

When people are ungrateful, how do you feel?

How does showing gratitude make the world a better place in which to live?

5. Up to this time Sara had refused to write to her parents in Europe. Miriam wrote to them but it wasn't the same as receiving mail from their daughter. Later that week—because she really wanted to write—Sara wrote a long letter telling her parents how happy she was in camp. She described all that had happened. One thing that pleased her parents most was Sara's apology for the way in which she had behaved when camp opened. Knowing that Sara was enjoying herself lifted a great burden from their shoulders.

Why do you think Sara wanted to write to her parents?

6. Sara discovered that helping other people to be happy made her happy, too.

Why?

Can you remember a time when helping someone made you happy?

Does Sara's problem remind you of yourself? Of a friend?

Who helped you? How? Did the help that you received change you in any way?

What did Miriam mean when she said that Sara had "won"?

Do you like Sara better now?

7. In the Midrash, the Rabbis tell us that when the people of Israel saw the Egyptian Army pursuing them, they were panic-stricken. They wanted to go back to Egypt. Moses stopped to say a long prayer asking God to save His people. God said, "Moses, My children are in trouble. The sea blocks them in front and the enemy is behind them. Yet you stand here and pray. Sometimes a long prayer is good but sometimes a short prayer is better. This is a time for action. Stop praying now. Lead the people forward and I will save them."

How did the actions of Harold and Miriam follow God's advice to Moses?

Was what they did a prayer? Why?

Can you think of a time when God's advice to Moses helped you?

8. When the boys in Emes were helping Gramps in the plant nursery he told them something Ben Zoma, a Rabbi in the Talmud, once said. "Observe how Adam worked. In order to eat a piece of bread he had to plow, sow, reap, thresh, and bake. I rise and find it all prepared for me. In order to have clothes, Adam had to shear the wool, dye it, spin, weave, and then sew. I find my clothes ready for me—all because of a group of workers."

What things do you take for granted?

How do groups of people working together make the world a good place in which to live?

What has this to do with the gratitude we show to God and to each other?

9. JOSHUA

Emes awoke one morning like a swarm of buzzing helicopters with a bad case of measles. Every face was covered with red spots—all except Ben's. It didn't take long to discover that the spots were made of lipstick. Ben's unmarked grinning face told them who was guilty. In the early morning he had crept from bed to bed dotting each face lightly.

The dotted faces stared accusingly at Ben.

"You pirate!" yelled Michael.

"Who? Me?" Ben asked innocently.

"At him, fellows!" shouted Jeff.

With a whoop the whole bunk piled on top of Ben, pummeling him until he yelled for mercy. Bill came to the rescue. "Quit the rough stuff, boys," he said, pulling Ben up from the floor. "We don't want anyone hurt before the big baseball game, do we?"

The warning worked like magic. Everyone scrambled to his feet. Camp Milford across the lake was playing the Y'lodim today. Excitement crackled in the air.

Ben dangled a rabbit's foot before Michael. "Here, Michael,

rub your hand on this. It'll bring us luck. Those Milford boys play a tough game. We're going to have a fight on our hands."

Steven grabbed the rabbit's foot and rubbed it against his chin. "Bring us luck, footsie, we need it," he pleaded. He turned to Ben and asked, "Can I wear it on my belt during the game? Please?"

"Nothing doing! Where I go, rabbit's foot goes!" Ben snatched the fur away.

"But I'm the captain and I should wear it," insisted Steven. He appealed to Bill for help. "Shouldn't I carry the rabbit's foot, Bill?"

Bill came over with a smile. "Are you going to depend on a rabbit's foot to win a game?"

"We don't need a rabbit's foot," said Joshua, "Steven's a champ, and when Ben wallops that ball, it goes places." Joshua's faith in his bunkmates made his face shine.

Ben dropped the fur into his trunk. "Thanks for the plug, Josh." He peered into the trunk. "As for you, my little footsie, we don't need you for a victory."

After breakfast, Roy, the head counselor, Gramps, and all the Y'lodim gathered around the flagpole. First, Roy outlined the plans for the day. "Each one of you will be responsible for a Milford guest," he said. "I don't have to tell you how we treat visitors here at Kee Tov. You know the right way."

Roy turned to Gramps, "How about a story to start the day?" he asked. When Gramps agreed, the Y'lodim cheered and cheered.

Gramps cleared his throat and began. "The Midrash loved to exaggerate Abraham's hospitality. It insisted that no one in all of Jewish history offered it in quite the same way. Surrounding his home were four gates, facing north, south, east, and west. No traveler had to go out of his way to enter Abraham's home. If the visitor needed food, Abraham gave it to him. If he needed clothes, Abraham provided that, too. If he needed silver or gold, he received what he needed for his journey. After the travelers had eaten and rested, they would try to thank Abraham. But he never allowed them to thank him. 'Thank God, instead of me,' he told them, 'for God alone provides food and drink for all creatures.' "

Gramps finished his story and Roy continued. "In our day we don't have to do quite what Abraham did—but like Abraham we can receive our guests with friendship, and guide them about the camp with true Kee Tov hospitality."

The Y'lodim clapped for Roy and Gramps.

"And one thing more," added Roy. "Kee Tov has always lost and won its games with good will, and that about winds up my talk. Good playing, boys!"

Joshua's guest was Peter Cohen. When Peter spied Joshua's white cane his heart sank. What fun could he have with a blind boy? But it didn't take Joshua long to change Peter's mind. Soon they were laughing together and Peter felt as if he had known Joshua for a long time. Of all the things at Kee Tov, Peter liked the silver Tree of Life best. "That's a wonderful tree," he said. "I wish we had one at Milford."

Joshua was pleased. "Why don't you suggest the idea to your camp council?" he said. "Maybe they'll make one, too. We look forward to Friday when Aaron awards the Torahs. It's the very best time of the week."

"I think I will," said Peter, who had already made up his mind to introduce the idea.

When they finished their tour Joshua asked Peter if he had any questions. Peter hesitated for a moment and then said, "I've been wondering about you. How do you know so much about Kee Tov?"

Joshua laughed. "I have many eyes, on the tip of each finger, and on the point of each sneaker. My cane is an eye and I have an eye right in the middle of my brain. That's the most important one of all because it tells the other eyes what to do. I'm like a beetle with many feelers, only I've lost two of them."

After lunch everyone gathered on the ball field.

The game was fast. After the third inning the score was 4 to 2 in favor of Camp Milford. Kee Tov was at bat with all the bases loaded.

"Ducks on the pond, Michael!" shouted Steven. Michael walked to the batter's box. His stomach tightened into a hard knot. It was up to him to bring the boys home.

The Milford pitch came in low and Michael swung. But it was too late!

"Strike one!" shouted the umpire. Back to the pitcher went the ball.

This time the pitch was too fast. Michael's bat stuck to his shoulder like glue.

"Are you playing ball or hopscotch?" shouted Steven from third base.

Michael made up his mind to hit the next ball no matter what happened. He dug his feet into the dirt and gripped the bat. This time the pitch was inside and Michael had to jump to one side to let the ball speed past him. He swallowed. Why couldn't he hit it?

"Ball one!" shouted the umpire.

Michael flushed red as a tomato. He yanked the visor of his cap. Again the ball rushed toward his chest but this time the bat greeted the ball like an old friend. Crack! Away it flew as Michael sprinted to first base. The second baseman caught the ball with a high jump. Plop! Michael saw the Milford boys drop their gloves and run to home plate. He had made the third out!

Steven dashed over to Michael, his eyes flashing. "For a guy who's always full of ideas, you sure play a stupid game. You chicken out every time the ball comes near you. Didn't you learn anything when I helped you all week?"

Michael stepped back as if he had been hit. But he tried to calm Steven. "I tried my best. Stop worrying! We'll make a recovery. The game isn't over yet. *Simmer down!*"

"If you were the captain, you'd try a lot better. But I'm the captain, so you don't care. Do you?" shouted Steven, pushing his face close to Michael.

Michael walked away. What a sorehead Steven was! Michael hoped the visitors wouldn't hear him sound off like that. He didn't want them to judge Kee Tov friendship by Steven's temper.

The game continued. The score was a tie now. Kee Tov was at bat again and it was Ben's turn. Picking up the bat, he grinned. "Watch me murder the ball!" A fast pitch came toward him and he swung. A sharp crack and the ball zoomed over the center fielder's head. The crack sounded like sweet music to Joshua's ears. Leaping from the side bench, he screamed, "That's our boy!"

Around first—and second—and third ran Ben, puffing and huffing. His round-as-a-barrel body was like a tired engine climbing up a mountain. "Where are my roller skates?" he called between huffs and puffs.

The outfielder scooped up the ball and hurled it to the short-stop, who whipped it to the catcher. Ben saw the ball coming just as he neared home plate. Stirring up a cloud of dust he slid home—but he was tagged out a second before he made it. Kee Tov was out and the inning was over.

Steven came running over, "You clown! Why didn't you run? You could have made it easily—but no! You have to make jokes!" Hurling his cap to the ground, Steven stalked off the field to the benches. His team followed him slowly. Plunking himself on the bench, Steven stormed at everyone. Suddenly, turning to Joshua, he said, without thinking, "You should be playing, Josh! Even without eyes you could have done a whole lot better!"

Michael jerked Steven's arm roughly. "Watch it, Steven! Joshua's not to blame if we make the outs, so don't go taking your temper out on him. And I told you once already—it's only a game!"

"That's the trouble with all of you! You keep making excuses for your bad plays, saying it's only a game. Well, I'm the captain of this baseball team and when the team loses, I'm responsible!"

Jeff interrupted. "You ought to have your ears laced back. The Milford boys are looking at us. If they get wind of this argument—what are they going to think of Kee Tov?"

Steven couldn't think straight. "Don't worry about them. They're winning! If they were losing, they wouldn't be good sports either. Just remember that!"

Joshua touched Steven's shirt. "You'd better calm down. Remember what Roy said about good losers." Joshua's face signaled a warning. Steven couldn't stop his rush of words. He knew they were cruel. But they whipped out before he could stop them. "What do you know about it? You've never played ball in your life."

A stunned silence followed. At that instant the umpire called for the next inning to begin. The boys dragged themselves out on the field, their feet numb and their hearts heavy.

Just as they were beginning the inning Jeff yelled from third base and stopped the game. "They've hatched! They've hatched! Look!"

Everyone came running. Behind the wall the Giborim had built, Jeff pointed to four downy birds, newly hatched. The babies huddled near their broken shells cheeping at the world with wide open beaks. The wonderful sight loosened the tight insides of the boys. Jeff put back the wall and the game continued.

Joshua left the field and walked slowly toward the Big House. He couldn't shake the unhappiness that filled every part of him. What had he done to make Steven lash out at him like that? Did the rest of the boys feel that way?

In the Thinking Place he called to Gramps but he wasn't there. Sitting on a log he rested his head on his hands. What a fool he had been to think the boys had thought of him as an equal. Now he knew they only felt sorry for him because he was blind. And all the time he had thought that he was turning into a good camper. What was he going to do? The thought of calling his parents and asking them to take him home brought tears to his eyes. He had been so happy at Kee Tov—happier than ever before in his life.

He began to walk toward the deep woods. Along the path he wandered, tapping his cane before him. Suddenly, he felt a wet nose in his hand. A sharp yip told him that Lovon had followed him. Bending down, Joshua hugged him. "You're the only friend I have, Lovon," he said.

Lovon trotted along beside him. Joshua found Lovon's collar with his free hand and held on to it, talking to the dog as if he were a friend. "I don't want to go home, Lovon. If I do, it'll mean that I'm running away. But—I don't want to stay here if the boys don't want me. And I don't want to be lonely again. It's the worst thing in the world to be lonely."

Lovon trotted beside the unhappy boy, gazing steadily up at him. He seemed to be telling Joshua he understood. He wagged his tail gently and edged closer to him.

They plunged deeper into the forest.

Back at the Emes cabin Steven faced Bill.

"You have to get straightened out, Steven."

"All I wanted to do was win the game," Steven tried to defend himself.

"Let's talk about what you did—man to man. You want to win. But you want to win so much you forget all about the other fellow. You don't care how the other boys are feeling or what they're thinking. You only think about Steven. It's *your* game and it's *your* championship."

"That's not so. I'm always helping the other guys. Didn't I help Michael?"

"Did you help Michael because you really wanted him to play better or because you wanted *your* team to win?"

Steven didn't answer.

"You can't set yourself up as a judge. What right have you

to be angry when Michael doesn't hit the ball or when Ben doesn't run fast? And you certainly have no right to be angry because Joshua is blind."

"Don't think I don't feel terrible about Joshua. I could have bitten my tongue. Joshua's one of the best guys at camp. When I see him, I'll tell him I'm sorry. Gosh, I wouldn't hurt Joshua for all the world."

Bill could see that Steven was really sorry.

"Look, Steven. If you'd let yourself be part of the team instead of working for yourself, the boys would respect you more and you'd be a lot happier."

Michael knocked at the door. "Bill, I can't find Josh. I've looked everywhere." Michael sounded frantic.

Alarmed, Bill raced to the Big House to get help, Michael and Steven following.

Back in the woods, Joshua heard the sharp growl of thunder. A flash of lightning burst in the sky. Another clap of thunder made the earth tremble. A great gust of wind slashed at the trees, cracking some of the branches, and whipping them into the air. All at once the sky opened and sheets of cold rain poured down over Joshua and the dog. Beyond them, in an open clearing, Lovon saw a huge tree. He tugged at Joshua to follow him. Reaching the tree, they huddled together close to the trunk.

"We're lost, Lovon," said Joshua, shivering.

Suddenly, they heard a branch snap. Joshua froze. Heavy footsteps were approaching the tree. Closer and closer they came. Lovon whipped around in front of Joshua, barking a warning. He pressed against Joshua's legs, standing guard between the strange sound and his blind friend.

"Don't be afraid, Lovon," said Joshua, softly. "No one will hurt us." He gathered his courage and spoke out into the darkness. "Who's there? I'm lost. We belong to Kee Tov. I'm blind. Can you help us?"

A light flashed into their faces and a tall man bent over

them, exclaiming, "Bless my heart! What have we here?" The stranger's kind voice told Joshua help had come.

"Come with me," said the kind voice, "my cabin is over there beyond the clearing." Joshua began to cry and the man scooped him up into strong arms. He ran toward the cabin, Lovon following. At last they were safe!

Inside, the man introduced himself. "I'm Matt Johnson and this is my summer cabin." He peeled off Joshua's wet clothes and wrapped him in a huge towel, rubbing him until he was dry. He did the same to Lovon. As he worked, Matt kept up a running conversation to make Joshua feel at home.

While Matt was heating some soup, Joshua told him what had happened.

"When I saw you run under that tree with your dog, my heart almost stopped. Standing under a tree during a lightning storm is mighty dangerous. It's a good thing I was on the porch. I'll telephone Kee Tov and tell them you're safe." Matt brought the hot soup to Joshua. "Do you want me to feed you?" he asked in his deep voice.

Joshua smiled gratefully. "No thanks. I always feed myself."

Matt hung the wet clothes in front of the big fire in the fireplace. "If these don't dry, I'll find something for you to wear when we're ready to go back to Kee Tov." He turned around and chuckled. Joshua and Lovon were fast asleep. Picking up the sleeping boy he put him on a sofa nearby, and covered him with a blanket. When Matt rang Kee Tov he could tell by Aaron's shout of joy how upset the camp had been. Matt promised to bring Joshua and Lovon back as soon as they had awakened.

Later—much later—Matt drove to Kee Tov in his station wagon. The joyful welcome awaiting Joshua proved how wrong he had been. His bunkmates *did* want him—and Bill and Aaron, too. The boys laughed with relief and pleasure when they saw Joshua. He was almost lost in Matt's big bathrobe. Matt had hitched it up with safety pins, but that didn't help. "I bet I can

take you all into this bathrobe with me," said Joshua, with a grin. "My friend, Matt Johnson, is a *big* man." Joshua took Matt's giant hand.

Aaron and Bill shook hands with Joshua's rescuer and thanked him. At first Steven hung back, embarrassed. Finally he made himself walk over to Joshua. "I'm sorry I was mean to you, Josh. Please forgive me."

Joshua laughed. "Of course, Steven. I know you didn't really mean it. I shouldn't have run away. I was wrong, too." They shook hands with warm smiles.

Bill said to Matt, "Aren't you the Matt Johnson who played with the Giants?"

"That's right—I'm retired now. Getting a little too old for the Big League," Matt chuckled at himself and at the boys.

"Did you hear that, fellows?" said Aaron. "This is Matt Johnson, one of the greatest ball players baseball has ever known."

Matt's loud laugh rang out. "That's a mighty fine reputation to live down." The boys' eyes grew round as pie-plates. "Glad to know you, boys," Matt continued. "Say, I've just had an idea. I still love baseball and I miss playing. Josh tells me that some of you are having a bit of trouble. Now that I have plenty of time on my hands, if it's all right with your director—how would you like me to come down and give you a few pointers?"

The shouts were louder than the peals of thunder that had cracked through the sky a few hours earlier.

"Come down, any time, Mr. Johnson," said Aaron. "The boys have expressed their joy better than I can. You're very welcome. Plan to eat with us when you're here."

Later that night Jeff said to Joshua, "Weren't you afraid when Matt found you? He's a Negro, you know."

"Negro?" Joshua's laugh rang out merrily. "What's Negro, Jeff? I don't see color. I only see people. Matt Johnson is my friend—my brand new friend."

WHAT DO YOU THINK?

1. While Aaron was waiting for Matt and Joshua he had a long talk with Steven. Aaron said, "In the Talmud the Rabbis asked, 'Who is honored by God?' And their answer was, 'He who honors his fellow man.'"

What do you think the Rabbis meant by this answer?

How did Steven dishonor Michael? Ben? Joshua? The visiting Milford team?

Do you believe the excuse Steven gave for behaving as he did? Why? Why not?

Aaron said that Steven could no longer be the captain of the team.

Do you think this punishment was too easy? Too harsh? Why?

What punishment would you have given Steven?

Were the boys better off or worse off without Steven as their captain? Why?

If Steven changed his ways, would you allow him to be your captain again?

Do you think it will be difficult for Steven to change?

Have you ever had an experience like the Kee Tov Y'lodim?

What did you do to help? What did your friends do?

Did you find it easy to forgive the boy who caused the trouble?

How does this tie in with God's commandment, "Love your neighbor as yourself"?

2. Ben told David this story while they were waiting for Matt to bring Joshua back to Kee Tov. A few months before camp opened, a Japanese boy moved next door to him. He came from Tokyo and his father was a

research chemist. Tako, the Japanese boy, felt strange and lost in his new surroundings. Ben made friends with him within a few days and tried in every way he knew to make him feel at home. But when he introduced Tako to his gang, the boys weren't friendly. Tako was hurt and Ben decided to have it out with the gang. One boy said, "We won't allow him in our gang. He attacked us—remember Pearl Harbor?" Ben said, "That happened a zillion years ago and you can't blame the war on one boy." The gang still refused to include Tako in their fun. Ben was disgusted. "If you won't let Tako be one of the gang—you can count me out, too!" he said, walking away.

Do you think Ben was right or wrong? Why?

What would you have done?

What would Abraham in the Bible have done?

Do you think Ben should have asked his parents for help in solving the problem? What do you think Tako could have done to help Ben?

Choose the best solution and dramatize it. Say what you feel.

Write an ending to this incident.

In the Bible God commands us, "Love ye therefore the stranger; for ye were strangers in the land of Egypt."

Why did God give this commandment?

How did Ben obey it? Matt? Joshua? Aaron? The campers?

Since there are hotels and restaurants today, we don't have to give hospitality in exactly the way Abraham did. A child in a strange city needs friends. He needs someone to hold out a friendly hand.

Have you or someone you know ever had an experience where you helped a stranger in your home? At school? In your neighborhood? What happened?

What are some of the ways in which you can be a good host in your own home?

3. The Talmud also says, "Do not transfer your fault to your neighbor."

What does this mean to you?

Where in the story did Steven transfer his fault to someone else?

Was Steven facing the truth about himself? Why? Why not?

Why does facing the truth about oneself require courage?

How did Jeff and David show courage at the game?

What would you have said to Steven if he had talked to you as he did to his bunkmates?

4. In the Bible we read that Jeremiah, the prophet, spoke out against the evil he saw around him. Because of his courage, Jeremiah was thrown into a lime pit by the king's princes. Ebed-Melech, a Negro servant in the palace, had the courage to speak to King Zedekiah. "My Lord, you are doing a great wrong, treating Jeremiah in this way. He will die of hunger." The king allowed Ebed-Melech to hoist Jeremiah to safety.

Which law in the Torah did Ebed-Melech obey?

How was Matt like Ebed-Melech?

Do you like Joshua's reply when Jeff said Matt was a Negro? Why?

Are people with dark skins any less God's children than people with white skins? Are they among the neighbors we are expected to love?

How can we help white and yellow and brown-skinned people live together in peace?

5. After the game Gramps told Steven this story from the Chasidic Rabbis: One day a rich man came to a rabbi in a small Russian town. The rabbi knew that the wealthy man was a miser refusing to share his riches with the needy. He tried to help him to change his ways.

The rabbi took the man by the hand and drew him to a window in his study.

"Look out there. What do you see?"

"People going about their business," answered the man, puzzled.

The rabbi then led the man to a mirror. "What do you see now?"

"Myself!"

The rabbi said, "Behold! The windows are glass and in the mirror there is glass. As soon as the silver is added, you stop seeing the other people."

Gramps smiled at Steven and asked, "Can you begin to scratch off a little of your silver, Steven?"

Why was this a good story to tell Steven?

Can scratching the silver mean getting rid of selfishness? How?

How can this story help you?

10. OPERATION SPACE HAT

A gay bugle trill announced mail call.

Shortly afterwards, Marsha laughed and showed the girls a letter from her mother.

Dear Marsha:

```
    Daddy and I are ----------------.  You received
a package from ----------------.  In it was a
----------------.  If you want to know what belongs
in the empty spaces, write quickly.  We haven't
had a letter for four days.
                    With ------- and --------,
                                        MOTHER
```

Miriam handed Marsha a pencil and paper. "You don't do another thing until you write, my pet."

"I've been so busy with our skit for tonight. Golly, time flies at Kee Tov." Marsha tapped her forehead. "What could be in that package? Who sent it?"

"Write and find out!" said Miriam.

A bubble of laughter escaped from Ann. "I asked Mother to tell me my worst fault for 'Admit Your Fault Day' and she wrote back ten. I have to take my pick." Ann studied them carefully. She didn't agree with her mother at all. Funny thing! At Kee Tov she didn't do wrong things at all. But it was different at camp.

"Read your faults to us," demanded Susan.

"That would be giving my secrets away," laughed Ann. She hid the letter in the bottom of her trunk.

Sara studied the colorful postcards from England. "Mother and Daddy have a surprise for me. They've sent it from Switzerland. They are so glad I'm happy at Kee Tov now." Sara passed the cards around.

Tamar's letter had two happy faces drawn at the bottom. One showed a sketch of her mother and the other, one of her father. Under the faces her father had written, "This is how we will feel when we see you on Visiting Day." Tamar looked gratefully at Sara. "They're so proud of me, now that I've passed the crib test—thanks to you."

Susan grunted with disgust when she opened her package. She drew out ten flash cards. It didn't take long to recognize the multiplication dragons that always confused her. At the end of her letter her mother had written, "You promised to take these cards to camp and study them all summer. I found them in the back of your bureau drawer. I'm sure you can find a few minutes each day for them—so—please—*study!*"

"Multiplication! Bah!" growled Susan, tossing the cards on her bed. "I hate arithmetic!"

Miriam picked up the cards. She remembered a teaching trick she had once used in school. With tape she pasted the cards to the wall in ten different places. The girls giggled.

"There's a fault for you, Susan," laughed Marsha, "you don't like arithmetic!"

Susan chased Marsha around the cabin, shouting, "I'll 9 × 6 = 54 you if you don't quit teasing me."

"And I'll 8 × 7 = 56 you if you dare to touch me," giggled Marsha, ducking out of Susan's reach.

"And I'll $9 \times 7 = 63$ both of you if you don't stop," said Miriam, with a grin.

The multiplication dragons rolled around the cabin. The girls began and ended their sentences with them. Marsha wrote about the fun in her letter. She knew her mother would be glad. Marsha had trouble with multiplication, too.

On the way back from mailing her letter, Marsha found Michael waiting for her.

"What's my worst fault?" he asked her.

"Being a boy!"

"Big joke! Come on, help me out!"

"Do you have any faults? I thought you were perfect."

Michael ignored his sister's remark and thought out loud. "Let's see. I hate to go to bed, and I lose my temper sometimes, and I'm afraid to hit the ball when I'm at bat."

Marsha stamped her foot. "Not wanting to go to bed isn't a bad fault and everyone is afraid sometimes."

Michael pulled Marsha's pony tail. "Thanks, Sister dear, I know exactly what to write, now." He raced away leaving Marsha with a wide open mouth.

Inside the cabin Marsha found everyone busily writing. When they had sealed their envelopes they handed them to Miriam. Miriam wrote a fault for herself, too. The girls couldn't imagine Miriam doing anything wrong.

"You haven't any faults, Miriam," said Tamar. "You're perfect."

"Only God is perfect, Tamar. There's plenty of room for improvement in me."

At eleven o'clock, the campers gathered in the chapel. Gramps was in charge. "Every year we hold this ceremony at Kee Tov. On this day we ask you to look into your hearts and think about your faults, the faults that keep you from helping yourself and your neighbor. No one reads your papers. It is your secret. We hope that you will face the truth about yourselves and work hard to solve your own particular problem." Gramps smiled at the earnest faces before him. "In the Bible we read, 'The seal of God is truth.' When we face the truth about ourselves, we are working with God as His partners."

Roy called the names of the boys' bunks. Into a basket went all the envelopes. Dot called the girls' bunks and into the basket went theirs, too. The counselors and Aaron dropped in their envelopes. When Gramps put one in, too, the campers gazed with wide-eyed wonder.

Gramps continued, "The Talmud says, 'Do not blame your fault on your fellow man.' Sometimes we blame the wrong things we do on the other person. We forget to place the blame where it belongs—on ourselves."

Gramps paused with a twinkle in his eyes and addressed the faults in the basket. "O ye faults. Listen well to all of us. We are going to try with all our might to get rid of you, and if, at summer's closing, we have licked you, then we will be able to say truly—Kee Tov!"

Gramps gazed steadily at the children. "Kee Tov?" he asked.

"Kee Tov!" agreed the campers with happy voices.

Later, in the Arts and Crafts Shop the girls were getting ready for their skit. It was called "Operation Space Hat." Marsha was the announcer and the rest of the girls were the models.

In back of the room Ann and Susan were talking together. "I wish I had a speaking part in our skit," said Susan, pasting some shiny leaves on an ice-cream carton.

Ann pulled at the door of the bird cage she was holding. She tossed her head at Susan.

"Our skit! It's not our skit! It's Marsha's—she's the whole show! Just because she wrote it she thinks she owns all of us. Always running around telling us what to do and how to do it and when to do it. I'm sick of her bossiness!" The door of the bird cage snapped off in Ann's hands. "I'm all thumbs today," she added, with a grumble.

They looked up to see Marsha racing towards them. "When

you come out on the stage," Marsha said, "I think you ought to walk up and down like real fashion models."

"You don't have to tell us what to do, Marsha," said Ann, sharply. "We know!"

Susan spread her arms wide and turned slowly. "Is this the way Your Highness wishes it?" she asked, sweetly.

Marsha stared at them. "Don't you like the skit any more? When I read it you screamed with laughter. You said it was the best skit you'd ever heard. Didn't you mean what you said?"

"It's a wonderful skit," said Ann, quickly. She didn't have the courage to tell Marsha what was bothering her. Marsha would think she was jealous. She really wasn't—she just thought that Marsha was too bossy.

Tamar called to Marsha to inspect the scenery she was painting. Marsha watched Tamar erase a line and draw it over four times. "You don't have to be so fussy, Tamar," she said, admiring the bright red space ship with spacemen, fat as balloons. "It's wonderful!"

"I can't help it. It's the same old trouble. My hands don't want to do what my head tells them to do."

Sara put down her paint brush. Taking Tamar's hand she pulled her away from the painted space ship. When they studied the canvas from a distance, Tamar was pleased. "The farther away you go, the better it looks," she admitted to Sara.

"That's how the campers will see it," laughed Sara.

Marsha wasn't listening. She couldn't forget what Ann and Susan had said. What had she done to make them act that way? But there wasn't time to worry now. She had to get the gold paint her mother had sent her. She ran as fast as she could to the cabin.

Ann and Susan walked up on the porch. Marsha couldn't help overhearing their conversation through the open window. Her face turned pale.

"I'm not going to be in that skit, Susan. I'm going to pretend I have a stomachache and go to the infirmary."

"You can't do that! You'll ruin the skit. Besides, you'd be telling a lie." Susan was afraid Ann meant what she was saying. "This is a S'goolo skit and you know we have to work together."

"No one will know if you don't tell!" said Ann.

"But, Ann. The skit won't be good if you're not in it. You *can't* do it! It's wrong!"

"Are you on my side or Marsha's? Let her skit be a failure. Who cares? Marsha wrote it. She's the big cheese and she can take the blame. Let her worry!"

"If you tell a lie and I keep quiet, then I'll be lying, too. I won't let you do it." Susan's refusal was final.

Inside, Marsha squirmed. The girls *were* angry at her. Why didn't they like the play? Had they lied when they said it was wonderful? What should she do? The problem loomed up before her like a huge wall. She remembered Daddy's words to Michael and herself. "Face up to your problem. Don't run away from it." She thought of the fault she had written. *"Don't be afraid to speak up when you must!"* All at once she knew what she had to do. Coming out from the cabin she faced the girls, feeling like Daniel in the lion's den. Both girls flushed!

"I didn't mean to listen but I couldn't help overhearing." Marsha's voice was quiet and sure though her heart was pounding.

The girls lost their tongues.

"If you didn't like the skit why didn't you tell me the truth? And Ann, I'm not going to let you pretend to be sick just to spite me. That's a silly trick and you know it!"

"What are you going to do about it? Tell Miriam?" Ann was suddenly afraid.

Susan pulled Ann's sleeve. "Wait a minute, Ann. You're so mad you can't think straight. Let's tell Marsha what's bothering us."

"Exactly what are you angry about? Because I wrote the play?" Marsha snapped.

"No, it isn't that," replied Susan, shaking her head. "It's

because we want speaking parts. Now all we do is walk around and you do all the talking."

It was then that Marsha realized how wrong she had been. She slapped her forehead. "Why didn't you tell me? I thought you'd be glad if I did all the talking. If I've been too bossy, then I'm sorry. The skit would be a flop without you!" Marsha was determined to straighten out the problem now that she knew what it really was.

Ann said nothing. A feeling of shame came over her. She had been unfair. Would Marsha ever forgive her?

"What do you think we ought to do?" asked Marsha, eagerly.

"When we model our hats why can't we describe them ourselves?" asked Susan.

Marsha's face lit up. "Of course! That's a dandy idea! Do Tamar and Sara feel the same way?"

"I don't know," replied Susan. "They didn't say anything to us."

"Let's get them and talk about it. The play will never be any good if our hearts aren't in it." Marsha felt better. She was glad she had brought the whole thing out in the open.

When Miriam arrived, she found them huddled together. She saw Marsha hand each girl a paper. "The girls want speaking parts—that is, all but Tamar—but we've made her change her mind. We're going to tell about our own hats," Marsha told Miriam.

Susan listened to Marsha's explanation. What a good sport she was! She could have told Miriam how unfair they'd been.

Ann couldn't stand it any longer. She told Miriam everything. Turning to Marsha, she said, "I haven't been a good friend, have I?"

Miriam didn't give Marsha a chance to answer. "Did you write that fault on the paper you put in the basket, Ann? It's no secret now."

A guilty flush appeared on Ann's face. Taking her courage in hand she made another confession. "I didn't tell the truth then either. I said I didn't like spinach—I don't—but that's not really a fault. I should have chosen from the list Mother sent. She knows."

"Why don't you write one down again and give Gramps the envelope," suggested Miriam. "You'll feel better."

In a short time Ann was on her way to see Gramps.

s'GOOLO PRESENTS * * * OPERATION SPACE HAT!

Marsha danced out from behind the painted space ship, her red cape billowing behind her like Superman's. "Good evening, all you lovely earth people. We are happy to bring you the newest atomic hats directly from a fashion show that took place on the moon last month." She danced back behind the space ship. Out came Ann, prancing forward to the gay piano music Miriam was playing.

On Ann's head was a golden bird cage topped with three carrots nestling in a bed of lettuce. She walked across the stage, opening and shutting the shiny door. With a fluttery giggle she spoke into the microphone. "My name is Atomic Ann and my hat is called the Bird Cage Look. What a sensation it made with the moon ladies! This supersonic glitter on my hat is guaranteed to keep my hat fresh for a hundred years. If you find that hard to believe, come and see for yourselves." Ann giggled again. And just as she disappeared behind the space ship, she shouted, "In a hundred years!"

Cheers rose from the campers.

Sara came next. On her head she wore a shiny green pie plate, in the center of which there stood a tin can. Copper scouring pads decorated the sides. Glued to the very top was a golden pine cone. The hat was tied under her chin with a green bow.

"I am Satellite Sara and my hat is called the Tin Can Tar Baby. The material is one of science's newest inventions— potato peel, porcupine quills, and green tar. It can be used as a pocketbook, too." Sara reached up to the can and pulled out a

lipstick and a huge powder puff. She scooted behind the canvas scenery as if she were being blasted. Peeking out a second later she shrieked, "Some thrust, too!"

Cheers rose to the tops of the trees.

Tamar faced the audience shyly. Miriam played a gay polka to give her courage. Attached to her head was an aluminum tray. Glued to it was a green toy automobile. Copper wire laced with marigolds fastened the tray firmly under her chin.

She could feel the butterflies bumping into each other in her stomach as she began to speak. "Tamar Telemeter is my name and this lovely model I'm wearing is the Cosmic Convertible. The material is a mixture of moon beam, moon glow, and moon struck. When you feel like taking a ride, just jump into my convertible and press the button." Tamar ran off the stage as if a lion were chasing her.

Cheers rose to the stars.

Out danced Susan with a yellow ice-cream carton perched saucily on her head. A flashlight stuck out of the top. She skipped across the stage turning her traffic light on and off. At the microphone she collapsed into giggles and the audience howled with her. "They call me Space Station Sue and my hat is known as the Flashlight Thrust. It can stop all traffic with its remote control switch. That uranium spark you see on top always tells my friends when I'm coming and going."

Cheers rose to the moon.

Marsha was next. Her wide blue felt hat had copper wires stretching out of the top like a television aerial. Attached to the wire ends were colorful cardboard space rockets.

"My name is Missile Marsha. This charming model you see is the Copper Orbit. It's made with boiled cheese, fried milk, creamed prunes, and baked tiger teeth. Do all of you find it hard to believe that such beauty can be made from this combination?"

"Yes!" yelled the campers.

Marsha bent down to whisper loudly to the audience. "I'm

going to let you in on a little secret. The Copper Orbit is copied from the new space station near the moon."

Cheers rose to split the sky.

Miriam played some more music and S'goolo took a bow.

Ben ran to the stage with his camera. "Cheese!" he shouted.

"Cheese!" shouted S'goolo.

"And crackers!" added the campers.

WHAT DO YOU THINK?

1. Ann did as Miriam suggested. She wrote, "I must face the truth about myself. I must not lie." Ann told Gramps that if she had had the courage to face the truth about herself, she wouldn't have been in trouble. Gramps said that facing the truth about oneself took special courage. He then told Ann this story from the Bible.

   When Moses reached the border of Palestine he sent twelve princes to explore the new land and bring back any information they could find. The Midrash tells us that ten of these men had made up their minds to bring back false reports even before they had left. They were afraid that they would lose their power in the new land and preferred to live in the desert. If they could persuade the people to stay in the desert, they would keep their power.

   On their return, the spies reported that the new land was full of warlike giants who would wipe out the children of Israel. They frightened the people into a rebellion against Moses and God. The people wanted to return to slavery in Egypt rather than enter the Land that God had promised them.

   Two of the men, Caleb and Joshua, took their courage in their hands and spoke up to the frightened people. "The land is good," said Caleb and Joshua, "and the Lord has promised to be with us." Because Caleb and Joshua had faith in God, they entered the Promised Land. The rebellious people were punished. None of them were allowed to enter the land God had promised to them.

How was Marsha like Caleb and Joshua?

How was Susan like them?

What might Caleb and Joshua say to Ann to help her?

Is there any connection between courage and truth? What?

Can you think of a time when you had the courage to speak the truth in the face of great difficulty?

How did you feel?

Did you help anyone?

2. In our *Union Prayerbook* we read, "Lord, who shall dwell in Your holy Tabernacle? He who walks up-rightly, does righteousness, and speaks the truth in his heart."

   In Hebrew "truth in his heart" is known as Emes B'libo.

   Why is it important to have the words you speak match your thoughts?

   How did Ann break this commandment?

   Can you think of a time when someone you knew didn't practice Emes B'libo?

   How did you feel? What did you do about it?

   Was your trust in that person the same after that?

   How does Emes B'libo say, "Love your neighbor as yourself"?

   How does Emes B'libo say, "Kee Tov"?

3. In school Susan always earned excellent marks. She studied hard and was proud of her record. One day the arithmetic test was long and hard. When the time was up she still had one problem to finish. To make matters worse she discovered that she had crossed out one right answer and substituted a wrong one. Now she would get a poor grade. She knew that some of the other children in her class cheated. Some of them did the odd examples and others the even

ones. When the teacher wasn't looking, they passed the answers to each other. It wasn't fair! She never did that! She did her own work.

During lunch period while the children and teacher were out of the room, Susan opened the teacher's drawer. She found her test and corrected her mistake. She also did the unfinished problem. The next day the teacher told Susan that she had received the highest mark in the test.

Did Susan deserve the highest mark? Did she do the work herself?

Should she tell the teacher what she had done?

Should she tell the teacher what the other children were doing?

If you had seen Susan doing what she did would you have told the teacher? What would you have done?

What would be a good way to solve the problem for everyone in the class?

Has something like this ever happened in your class? How was it solved?

What harm does cheating do to you?

What is the difference between telling a lie and cheating? How are they the same?

4. After the skit the same night, Miriam told the girls this story from the Bible. She was delighted that Marsha and Ann and Susan had forgiven each other and worked out their problem peacefully.

Joseph's brothers were jealous of Joseph because Jacob, their father, loved Joseph best of all his sons. They decided to get rid of Joseph and sold him to a band of traders traveling to Egypt. Later they brought Joseph's bloody coat to their father and told him that Joseph had been slain by a wild animal.

Yet, years later, Joseph forgave his brothers completely for their wicked deed. When he saw how afraid they were that he would seek revenge, Joseph calmed them with these words: "Do not be ashamed of yourselves because you sold me. You meant it for evil but

God turned it to good. God sent me to Egypt so that you could live."

What did Joseph mean by this last sentence?

How was Marsha like Joseph?

Why is it important to forgive each other? How do you know that your parents and teachers are forgiving?

How did the discussion the girls had help to clear up their problem?

Do you think the skit was better because the girls worked together rather than against each other?

Was Marsha wrong in assuming that the girls wanted her to do all the talking? Where did she make her mistake?

What happens to a project when there is quarreling?

Have you had an experience when discussing and bringing the problem out in the open helped to solve a serious problem? Did it happen at home? At play? At school? How did it work out?

5. The Rabbis in the Talmud said these three things:
"See that your 'yes' shall be just and that your 'no' shall be just."
"The penalty of a liar is that when he tells the truth, no one believes him."
"If you tell a lie it becomes a habit."

What do they tell us about Emes B'libo?

Can you think of any playmates who have the habit of telling lies?

What kind of lies do they tell? Do you tell them that they are lying, or do you keep quiet? How can you help people like this?

Would helping people to tell the truth be "loving your neighbor like yourself"? What do you do when you can't tell whether what they say is true or not?

In the Talmud we also read, "You lie when you keep still when a lie is told."

How did Susan say the same thing in the story?

How does this apply to the child who helps another child to cheat?

How does this apply to the child who lies to cover up for someone in trouble?

Have you ever been with a child who lied about his age in the movies? In the bus? Is this Emes B'libo? Why is Emes B'libo so hard for a good Jew to do? Why is it so important? How can we learn to do it more and more?

11. MT. SINAI, NEW HAMPSHIRE

Before Michael opened his eyes that morning, he remembered something exciting was going to happen. At last! The big day had arrived! Emes was going on an overnight hike to the slope of Mt. Sinai across the lake.

Joshua was going, too. At first Aaron and Bill had thought the trip would be too dangerous because of the narrow mountain trail. Disappointed, the boys had gone in a body to see Aaron. "We'll be Joshua's eyes," pleaded Michael for all of them. "How could he possibly get hurt with five pairs of eyes watching him all the time?"

Aaron had been firm. After he had pointed out the dangers, the boys went away with heavy hearts. But Matt Johnson had saved the day. Approaching Aaron, he had said, "How would it be if I took Joshua in my station wagon to the camping site and met the others there? That way Josh will be able to enjoy most of the trip and still be safe."

Aaron had finally given permission. How Joshua's face had beamed! Then the boys realized how much he'd really wanted to go. Yet he hadn't complained once. Michael looked fondly at the quiet sleeping face beside him. What a wonderful friend Josh was. He helped everyone. Sometimes when Michael felt himself getting angry, all he had to do was look at Josh's calm face, and the anger left as quickly as it came. Funny how Josh's contentment affected others.

The boys had worked like beavers learning to master the woodcraft skills. Bill had insisted that they pass a woodcraft test. Steven had been first to pass. Michael and Jeff had passed the next week. Even Josh had learned how to get his sleeping bag ready. But Ben had failed again and again. His bed roll always looked lumpy and whatever he cooked ended up in the fire. Bill had to postpone the hike until Ben had passed the test.

That was where the trouble with Steven had begun. When he heard that Ben was the reason for the postponement, Steven exploded. "Why don't you get down to business and stop the clowning, you hammerhead? If you'd stop cracking your corny jokes and put your mind on learning woodcraft, maybe, *maybe* we'd go on that hike before the summer ended!"

"I guess I'm just not as smart as you are, Steve," Ben had said, grinning.

Michael admired Ben for being so good-natured when Steven criticized him. Ben had a way of laughing everything off, particularly Steven's remarks. If Steven talked that way to *him*, Michael knew *he* wouldn't be so good-natured.

In the middle of all these recollections, Michael dozed off again. All at once the alarm clocks went off—all at the same time. The boys had insisted on setting all the clocks last night. What if Bill's didn't work! They weren't taking any chances.

After breakfast they found Matt at their cabin stowing the camping gear in the back of his station wagon. Lovon was following him, barking at his heels.

"Don't forget the bottles for the moth hunt," reminded Jeff, handing Matt a case from the porch. Jeff had persuaded Bill to take them on a moth hunt so they could mount a collection for Parents' Day.

The hike began. They rowed across the lake and beached the boat on the other side. The trail rose sharply and led into a dark pine forest. After an hour of steady climbing, Ben halted. "Let's rest a while, Bill. I'm out of breath." Beads of perspiration dotted his forehead.

"Time for a breather!" called Bill.

Steven grumbled, "But Bill, I'm not tired. We'll never get to the camp site if we waste time!" Steven pointed to Ben aiming his camera at a jewel weed clump. "Ben's not too tired to snap pictures!"

"We're not going on until Ben gets some rest, Steven. We can all use some. This is a bunk hike and all of us are going to enjoy ourselves." Steven was quiet.

After a most welcome fifteen-minute halt they continued their climb.

Bill started a hiking song. Their loud, happy voices startled the birds from their roosts. The trail became steeper. Bill made them rest more often now. When they came to a mountain stream tumbling merrily over the rocks, they paused to drink the cool water and wash their warm faces.

"Let's eat here," said Bill, putting down his knapsack. The hungry boys needed no urging.

A small chipmunk making a big noise nosed close to the carrot Ben was holding. Its eager eyes made Ben place the carrot on the ground. Out came two paws to snatch up the carrot. The boys laughed when they saw the chipmunk sitting on its haunches munching the carrot as if it were an ice-cream cone. Ben snapped the picture. "I'll call it, 'Carrot Ice-Cream,'" he laughed.

Higher up on the slope they found a mountain lake gleaming like a mirror in the sun. When they came close they looked with wonder at a mother bear swimming in the lake. A baby cub hung onto her tail, clutching with all its strength. Ben ran to the spot where he could get the best picture.

"See him run!" said Steven, scornfully, "he's not tired now.

I'm sick of that stupid camera. I wish it would fall into the lake."

Michael flared at Steven, "Why don't you stop picking on Ben? He's not hurting you! I bet you won't refuse the pictures Ben promised us when he develops them."

"Who wants his old pictures, anyway?" answered Steven, with a shrug. He walked slowly away. Why did Michael always defend Ben? When Michael looked at him after he criticized Ben, Steven always felt uncomfortable. How he wished he could like Ben as the other boys did. But Ben always annoyed him. He just didn't like Ben's corny jokes! They weren't the least bit funny! What a dumb guy! He couldn't even learn a few woodcraft skills.

When Ben returned, Jeff said, "If you meet a bear, introduce yourself to him. Maybe he'll invite you to dinner." Jeff's eyes twinkled with mischief.

Ben chuckled, "No, thanks! I'd make too tasty a meal for a bear."

At four o'clock they reached the camp site.

They looked down upon mountains ranged like misty blue dragons with curly backs. Soon they heard the station wagon grind to a stop. With wild whoops they ran to welcome Matt and Joshua.

Matt pulled down the back of the station wagon and everyone stared at a big burlap bag. It was wiggling and churning with motion. They saw a nose, then a soft curly head with two mischievous eyes emerge from the bag. It was Lovon!

With a yap the dog leaped up on Michael, knocking him over. Lovon shoved Steven, Ben, Jeff, and Joshua on top of Michael. Leaping from boy to boy like a giant white grasshopper, Lovon licked their faces with joyful barks. He paused, panting, to gaze at Matt and Bill who stood silently, frowning at him. But no one could be cross for very long atop that beautiful mountain! Lovon watched the frowns change to smiles, his tail wagging happily.

After the camp was set up they explored the trails around them. At the top of one trail they gazed with wonder at the sight spread before them. A roaring waterfall dropped a curtain of water over a huge cliff. It splashed into a stream below. In the West above the purple mountain stretched a wide band of crimson.

Bill said, "The heavens declare the glory of God."

Matt finished the quotation. "And the firmament showeth His handiwork."

Bill began to sing. His Hebrew song of praise echoed across the mountain.

"*Mi chomocho bo-elim Adonoi? Mi komocho ne'dor bako-desh? Noro s'hilos o-se fele.*" The boys joined him.

Matt closed his eyes and listened to the ancient melody. Bill translated the Hebrew words for him: "Who is like unto Thee, O Lord? Who is like unto Thee, glorious in holiness, awe inspiring, working wonders?"

"I know just how you feel," said Matt in a deep voice. "Up here on the top of the world you begin to know how small you are in the midst of God's glory."

"And now let's see how much you fellows have learned about cooking," said Bill, breaking the silence that followed Matt's remark.

Back to camp they raced.

Soon the fire was burning evenly. It took a long time for the boys to gather the right green sticks for cooking. Ben found three long, strong sticks and gave one each to Joshua and Bill. Michael found one for Lovon and one for himself. Jeff took care of Matt. When Steven saw the extra sticks he slapped his forehead. He had been so busy looking for his own he had forgotten all about the others. Running back into the woods he soon came back with six more. "I bet these are the best sticks around here," he boasted.

Matt and Bill removed the aluminum foil wrapping from the

steaks they had brought and placed them on a tree stump until they were ready to start broiling them.

Steven wove his stick through the steak and held it above the glowing coals. He turned it over, cooking it slowly. Michael fixed Joshua's steak and then he fixed Lovon's. The dog's tongue was hanging out in anticipation. Matt stood guard on Joshua's right side and Bill on his left. Their eyes never left Joshua's hands as he cooked his own steak over the fire.

Ben decided to dance a gay jig while holding his stick over the coals. The jig ended with a bump against Steven. This sudden jerk sent Ben's steak plunging into the coals with a sizzle. "My steak!" yelled Ben. He tried to poke it out with his stick, but it was too late. He had to drop the stick when it began to flame.

"You mousebrain! How clumsy can you get?" shouted Steven. "What are you going to eat now?"

Ben mournfully watched his steak turning black in the fire and scratched his head. "Guess I'll have to kill a bear," he finally said with a grin.

Bill laughed. "Accidents can happen," he said. "It so happens that Joe gave us some extras for just such an emergency."

"I'd better fix the next one for you, Ben," said Matt, spearing a steak on another green stick. Soon he was holding Ben's steak in one hand and his own in the other.

"That's Ben all over," whispered Steven to Matt, "always letting the other guy do his work for him." Before Matt could answer, Steven turned to Ben and asked, "Why don't you take a picture of your steak on the fire?"

"That's a dandy idea," agreed Ben, with his usual good nature, "and I'll call the picture, 'The Steak That Got Away.'" Ben ran for his camera.

Everyone laughed except Steven. He bent over his steak. His face looked like a volcano about to erupt. How foolish he felt! Ben always managed to turn everything Steven said into a joke.

Why did Ben make him say those things? Why didn't he ride the other boys? Why only Ben? He shrugged his shoulders making up his mind to keep quiet no matter what!

Suddenly one of the potatoes exploded like a firecracker. Again Steven couldn't stop the words that rushed to his lips. "That must be your potato!" he stormed, pointing an accusing finger at Ben. "Don't you remember Bill telling us to stab the potato so that the steam could escape?"

Jeff burst into laughter. "You're wrong, Steven. I was the one who forgot."

"The least you can do is apologize to Ben," said Bill, looking at Steven's flushed face.

"I'm sorry," said Steven grumpily, feeling foolish again.

*   *   *

Later that night the boys went on a moth hunt. Following the golden arcs of their flashlights they trooped single file into the woods. Sitting quietly near a giant walnut tree they waited, their faces drawn with excitement.

The boys had to smother their giggles when they saw Michael's flashlight in Lovon's mouth. He looked like a white car with one lonely headlight.

Soon dozens and dozens of moths fluttered around them. The boys watched with fascinated eyes and pounding hearts. A group of white luna moths danced around the walnut tree trunk, like graceful fairies against the dark leaves.

A humming bird moth dived like a bullet onto a sprig of moss near Jeff's hand. With a quick twist of the wrist, Jeff popped the moth into his "live" bottle. Quickly he placed the pierced cover on the bottle and patted the cotton batting around the outside into place. An io moth hovered over the moss near Jeff, its yellow and wine wings trembling in the air. With a soft cry of joy Jeff swooped the lovely io into his jar.

Ben's eagle eye saw a brown moth zooming above his head out of reach. Picking up his flashlight he shot it down with a beam of light. It zigged and it zagged trying to get away, but the beam held it like a magnet as it glided into the bottle. Ben laughed softly as he examined its tan and brown wings. In the center of each wing he noticed a single eye gleaming like a jewel. "What a beauty!" he said to Steven, showing him the moth through the open top partly covered with his hand.

"What luck!" said Steven, "I haven't caught a single moth yet."

"Here, I'll help you," offered Ben. And before Steven could get over his surprise, Ben had bagged another io into Steven's jar.

"Thanks, Ben." Steven examined his moth carefully. without meeting Ben's eyes. A feeling of shame began to spread through him. Gosh, Ben was swell! Here Ben was helping him, despite all the riding and criticism. Steven wanted to tell Ben how sorry he was for being mean, but the only words that came were, "Thanks again, Ben."

Ben waved the thanks away, his eyes searching for another moth.

"Hold your bottle ready," said Matt to Joshua, who was sitting quietly at his side. "I'll try to direct a moth into it with my flashlight." Joshua heard the flutter of a moth as it glided into his bottle. With a gay laugh he quickly closed the bottle. "What color is it?" he asked eagerly.

"White. Snow white!" whispered Matt into Joshua's ear.

All at once an apple gree with eyes like flashing rubies hung in the air above Michael's head. Michael pointed Lovon's headlight in its direction. The gree quivered, struggling to free itself from the powerful net of light. But its struggles were useless. Down coasted the moth into the bottle, its long green wings outstretched.

Michael laughed, "I bet you're the first dog on this planet to catch a moth with a flashlight," he said, patting Lovon.

When the boys had filled their live bottles they trooped back to the camp site. Everyone hustled about to build up the fire. Soon the flames were dancing gaily, pushing back the darkness. Michael felt as if he could touch the stars marching above his head like a parade of blazing soldiers.

Ben slapped at a huge mosquito. "These mosquitoes are big enough to saddle," he chuckled to Steven. "They jab me here and they jab me there trying to find the place where I taste the sweetest."

Steven laughed. For the first time Ben was funny! That's strange, he thought. He's really a funny kid. Did he laugh because Ben helped him to catch a moth? He bit his lips. Somehow he didn't feel so important any more.

"Tell us a story, Bill," said Michael, heaping some more wood on the fire.

"I have a story from the Midrash about Joshua—" said Bill, grinning when Josh flushed. "About Joshua in the Bible."

Bill waited for the boys to get comfortable before he began. "The rabbis tell us that when Moses discovered he could not enter the Promised Land, he prepared Joshua, his most trusted aide, for leadership. He did this in a strange way. He would arise at midnight and enter Joshua's tent. There he would serve Joshua as if he were a great and powerful king. He would shake the dust from Joshua's shirt and lay it neatly on the pillow. Next, he would clean Joshua's sandals and place them in readiness near the bed. He would prepare a pitcher of water and a basin so that Joshua could wash himself when he arose. He swept the tent in every corner.

"The Midrash tells us that Joshua was uncomfortable when Moses did these services for him, but Moses quieted his fears. 'Fear not, my son,' he said, 'you are not sinning when you allow me to serve you. You are my pupil and your honor is as dear to me as my own.'

"Moses then instructed his herald to ask the people to gather together near his golden throne. The people gazed in astonishment when Joshua, walking before Moses, mounted the throne. They saw Moses seat him on it. At first they refused to accept Joshua as their new leader and rebelled. But when Moses said, 'Whoever wishes to hear God's words must come to Joshua, for he is the leader in Israel,' the people accepted Moses' command. Thus did the humble Moses convince the people to listen to God's command."

The boys teased Joshua after the story. Ben volunteered to shine his shoes. Steven offered to get him some water. Michael brushed his shirt, and Jeff scratched his back. It ended in a free-for-all, with all the boys piling on top of each other. Bill and Matt had to come to Joshua's rescue.

Michael chased two ants off his arm. "You're not the only one who's sweet," he said to Ben. "These ants like me, too."

The ants reminded Bill of King Solomon and another story the rabbis told.

"In the Midrash we read that King Solomon was great and powerful, wise and just. Yet King Solomon had to be taught a lesson in pride, too. King Solomon had a magic carpet sixty feet square that carried him everywhere he wanted to go. Once as he was sailing through the air he boasted to himself, 'There is no one like me in all the world. God has not only given me wisdom and knowledge, but He has also made me ruler of the world.'

"Once on his travels King Solomon wandered into the Valley of the Ants. He knew the language of every living creature so he could understand what the Queen Ant said to her ant subjects when she called them to an ant council. 'Run quickly to your hiding places,' she told them, 'lest we be crushed by the armies of King Solomon.'

"The king called to the Ant Queen. When she drew near, he said, 'May I ask you a special question?'

" 'Not until you pick me up and place me in the palm of your hand,' replied the queen. King Solomon did as she asked.

" 'Now,' he asked her, 'is there anyone in this wide world greater than I?'

" 'Yes,' said the queen, calmly.

" 'How is that possible?' he asked in a puzzled voice.

" 'If I were not greater than you, God would not have led you to our valley so I could be placed in your hand.'

" 'Why did you say that?' asked Solomon, now ashamed of his boasting.

" 'Because I was afraid my ants would learn pride from you instead of being humble before God.' "

Bill paused for a minute and added, "This is how the rabbis taught that God is not happy with those who boast and brag about themselves. God is happy with those who are silent and let only their goodness speak for them."

Now the boys begged Matt to tell them some true baseball stories. It was late when he finished. The last thing Matt said was, "The best ball players help the rookies all the time. I've seen them spend many hours teaching the rookies the fine points of baseball that come only from experience—hours in which they might have rested." The boys knew without being told that Matt had always been one of those helpers.

* * *

Lovon awoke the next morning to see the dawn streaking across the sky. Up the trail he scampered to the waterfall, reaching it just as the sun was rising in the East.

Behind the waterfall at the bottom of the cliff Lovon discovered a passageway hollowed out behind the curtain of water. Through the tunnel he scampered to the other side of the rushing stream.

Here trouble hit Lovon squarely in the face.

He spied a fishing net with colored balls on the ground. He began to play with the balls and tangled himself in the net. The more he tried to free himself, the more snarled he became. But his furious growls were only a whisper compared to the roar of the waterfall. Struggling frantically, he tried to get loose but the net held him firmly imprisoned.

The boys discovered Lovon was missing when they returned

from a fishing trip. Bill decided to organize a searching party. Matt, Jeff, and Michael went into the woods. Ben and Steven tried the waterfall. Bill stayed with Joshua. He was taking no chances.

Ben and Steven followed the trail down to the bottom of the cliff. It wasn't long before Ben discovered Lovon's squirming body on the other side of the stream. They shaded their eyes with their hands to get a clearer view.

"Lovon's tangled up in something," said Ben. "Can you see him?"

"How did he cross that swift stream?" asked Steven.

Ben ran to examine the cliff near the waterfall. All at once he knew how Lovon had crossed. "Look, Steven, there's a tunnel here behind the falls. Let's go through. It looks safe."

Steven's eyes searched the waterfall. "It's too dangerous," he said, drawing back. "I'm not going!" Tugging at Ben's shirt, he tried to pull him away from the opening.

Ben shrugged himself free. "Lovon's in trouble. I *have* to help him." Ducking into the tunnel Ben found the path wide and dry. He heard Steven yell, "Come back, Ben! You'll get killed!"

Ben laughed. "It's as safe as a baby carriage," he called back.

But Steven didn't hear. He was rushing up the trail to get help.

On the other side, Ben ran to Lovon. Quickly, he untangled the net. At one place he had to cut the net with his jack-knife. "Steady boy! Steady boy!" he said. "I'll get you out of this mess." While Ben worked, Lovon sniffed every part of him, licking his face and barking happily. Finally the dog was free. He twirled around Ben like a pinwheel, yelping his thanks. Together they went back through the tunnel. This time Ben stopped to peer through the water curtain sparkling like diamonds in the sun. "I wish I had a picture of us here," said Ben. "What a prize shot that would be!"

When they came out they found everyone waiting. Michael ran over to Ben. "That was a brave thing to do, Ben. But you shouldn't have risked your life like that."

"Risk!" Ben exploded with laughter. "What are you talking about? That path behind the waterfall is wide enough for an automobile."

The boys looked at Steven, remembering how he had come into camp shouting. "Ben's going to be killed! He'll drown! He's trying to save Lovon on the other side of the waterfall!"

Bill looked at Matt and turned to Ben. "Just the same, Ben, you should have come for help before trying anything dangerous like that."

Ben shook his head impatiently. He insisted that Bill follow him into the tunnel and see for himself. Soon everyone was walking behind the water, looking out through the shining waterfall. Matt and Bill led Joshua inside, too. How he loved the feeling of the cool spray against his face.

Steven walked slowly back to camp. What was everyone going to think of him now? Would they call him a coward? He dreaded the teasing he would get when the boys returned. He certainly had been wrong about Ben. What if he couldn't cook a steak. Big deal! When it came to an emergency Ben followed through, not he. He felt himself growing smaller and smaller in his own mind. Never had he felt more foolish or ashamed. Now he knew what he had to do. He had to tell Ben how sorry he was for all the unfair things he had done and said to him.

Steven didn't know that Bill had told the boys not to tease Steven about the fear he had shown at the waterfall.

After lunch they started back to Kee Tov. It was too hard for Steven to face his problem. He asked Bill if he could ride back with Matt instead of taking the trail. He complained of a headache, which he really had. Bill knew right away how Steven was feeling. "Look here, Steve, are you ashamed because you were afraid?"

Steven lowered his eyes and kicked the pebbles under his feet. "Not only that, Bill. I guess I'm especially ashamed because I've been so mean to Ben, always picking on him because I thought I was smarter than he was. He's really a swell guy. He even helped me catch some moths last night."

"Why don't you tell that to Ben? You'll feel better."

"Ben isn't a coward like me. He certainly proved that."

Bill put his arm around Steven's shoulder. "You weren't a coward, Steve. You just didn't believe that tunnel was safe. Sometimes, where we're afraid, our thinking stops for a while. Now, what do you want to do? Will you finish the hike with us or do you still want to go back in the station wagon?"

"I'll go with the bunch," said Steven. "And Bill—I promise never to boast about myself again. You'll see—I really mean it!"

On the way down the slope Steven apologized to Ben.

One of the things he said was, "You were really the brave one, you know."

Ben stopped in surprise. "But Lovon was in trouble and I love that dog. There you go again, harping on the risk I took. It was safe, I tell you!"

"I guess I'm like King Solomon—always boasting," said Steven, suddenly knowing why Bill had told the story. "I needed a lesson just the way Solomon did."

Ben chuckled and slapped Steven's shoulder. "Do you have rocks in your head? I never heard of King Solomon playing championship baseball the way you do."

WHAT DO YOU THINK?

1. The next day Steven had a long, long talk with Gramps in the Thinking Place. The more Gramps talked, the more Steven understood why he had been wrong.

   "In the Bible," said Gramps, "it says, 'The man, Moses, was a meek man.' When God told Moses to go to Egypt to free his people, Moses argued, 'Who am I to go to the mighty Pharaoh? I am but a poor shepherd. There are richer and mightier men than I to be given this great work.'

" 'You are a great man, Moses,' replied God, 'and I have chosen you for this great task.'

"When God saw that Moses hesitated about accepting His offer, He said, 'Why do you hesitate? If you do not save your people, no one else will do it.'

"Moses had still another argument. 'O Lord, I am no speaker. I am tongue-tied. Never will I be able to find the proper words to say to Pharaoh.'

"God replied, 'Go! I will help you to speak and I will teach you what to say.' "

Another way of saying the same thing is found in the Talmud.

"The greater the man, the more aware he is of his faults."

Why is this true?

List the ways in which Ben was like Moses.

List the ways in the story in which Steven was not like Moses.

When did Steven begin to change so that he was more like Moses?

Gramps also told Steven a story from the Midrash in which the Rabbis told about God's humility.

"God showed His humility when he spoke to Moses from the lowly thorn-bush instead of from a stately cedar tree."

Gramps told Steven this story, too:

"When God created man He took dust from the center of the earth and dust from the four corners of the earth—red, black, yellow, white, and brown—and mixed it with water from all the oceans and seas. In this way God knew that all races of men would be included in the first man—so that no one could say he was better than the other."

What can you learn from these stories to help you "Love your neighbor as yourself"?

When the boys stood on the mountain with Bill and Matt and sang "Mi Chomocho" they felt their littleness amidst God's greatness.

Have you been in places where this feeling of humble-ness has come to you?

Appoint various children to prepare reports that tell about some of these places and read them to the class. Be sure to include a report on the Cathedral of the Pines in New Hampshire.

2. One day last spring Jeff's mother cut her hand while she was washing dishes. She asked Jeff to finish the dishes.

"Dishwashing's for girls," said Jeff. "What'll my gang say if they catch me doing such sissy stuff?"

"If it hurts your pride to help me," said his mother, "don't bother!"

"But I'm an athlete. I bring out the garbage and I mow the lawns—that's man's work!"

Jeff's Uncle Saul came in at that moment. He was a famous hockey player and Jeff admired him more than anyone in the world, next to his parents. When Uncle Saul saw the bloody hand and the dirty dishes he grabbed a towel. "Come on, Jeff! Let's get with it!" Jeff told him how he felt about doing the dishes. Uncle Saul said, "In the Army, men do the cooking. And doesn't your father help your mother with the household chores? So a boy helps his mother, that is—if he's really a man."

Why do you like Uncle Saul's answer to Jeff?

Has this ever happened to you? What did you do?

Did your mother let you get away with your reasons? Do you think she should have acted like Jeff's mother?

How does this story compare with the rabbi's statement, "Man was created on the sixth day so that if he is ever filled with pride, it can be said that a flea came before him in Creation"?

Whom did Jeff think more of—his mother or his gang?

What would you have said if you were a member of Jeff's gang?

How could the story about how Moses served Joshua help Jeff?

3. The Talmud tells us that Rabbi Simeon Ben Yochai, famous for his knowledge of the Torah, was once traveling to a city. He walked with his head high, swelled with pride, because of his great knowledge and wisdom. Elijah, disguised as an ugly old man, met him on the road and greeted him warmly. Instead of politely returning the greeting, Rabbi Ben Yochai turned on Elijah with these words. "How ugly you are! Are there other men in your city as ugly as you?"

Elijah looked at him calmly. "I don't know," he answered. "Why don't you complain to the Artist who made me?" The rabbi realized his great sin and begged Elijah to forgive him. Elijah refused and set off for the city gates, the rabbi following him. When they entered the city all the people were waiting to meet the famous teacher. Elijah pretended he did not know what they were doing and asked the reason for such a crowd. They told him the man who was following him was a great scholar of the Torah. The old man refused to believe it. Only when Simeon Ben Yochai told everyone what he had said and apologized for his sin did the old man forgive him and say he was a true rabbi.

In what way was the story of King Solomon and the Ants like the story of Rabbi Ben Yochai?

Why does the Talmud tell this story about a famous rabbi like Ben Yochai?

Can you see now why "meekness is a guard against speaking evil against your fellow man"?

Do you think that being smart is a good reason for acting in a proud manner to one who is not as smart as you? Why?

Is it an excuse for being rude? Why?

How does haughty behavior prevent people from obeying God's commandment?

Do you know anyone who acts this way toward you? What do you do? How do you feel? Do you find it hard to be friends with a person like this? Why?

How did Michael treat Steven's pride? Would you have done the same thing?

Did it take courage for Michael to say what he did to Steven—remember Michael was a little afraid of Steven's anger.

How did Michael show Emes B'libo?

How can you explain why Steven didn't complain about Joshua going on the hike? He knew that Joshua would hold them back as they climbed the trail. Yet he went with the boys to Aaron to beg him to let Josh go. Did Joshua's blindness have something to do with Steven's action?

Was Matt a humble man? How do you know?

List all the things that Matt did in the story that show us Matt "loved his fellow man."

4. One of the stories Bill told the campers at a Sabbath service was a legend from the Midrash. A wise father was unhappy because his only son refused to study. When the father was about to die he called his son to him. "When I die all my riches will be yours if you can prove that you can take care of it. To prove it you must go out into the world and find the greatest fool. When you find him, give him this golden apple."

   The son traveled from city to city and from town to town, year after year. But in all his wanderings he did not find the foolish man he was looking for. His hair turned gray and he became bent and old. Finally, he returned home to find his home in ruins and his father's wealth spent by faithless servants. All he had left was the golden apple. Too late, the son realized that he was the foolish man. Any man who would spend a lifetime searching for a fool was indeed a fool himself. As a lesson to proud men who judge other peoples' foolishness but do not judge their own, God put the son in the face of the moon. That is why the moon sometimes looks like a golden apple.

Why did Bill tell the campers this story?

What did Steven say about Ben that makes you think Steven thought Ben a fool? Do you agree with Steven? Why?

Is it easier to laugh at the jokes of someone you like? When did Steven laugh at Ben's jokes?

Do you think a person who laughs at his own mistakes is foolish? Why? How does making a mistake with good humor help us to grow?

How does getting angry at yourself when you make mistakes stop your growing?

Can you think of a time when your sense of humor helped you over a rough spot?

5. The Talmud tells us that they asked the fruit trees why they made no noise when the wind blew through them. The fruit trees answered, "Our fruits are enough advertisement for us."

    Another way of saying this is found in Proverbs in the Bible. "Let another man praise thee and not thy own mouth."

How had Steven changed at the end of the hike?

Do you like him better now? Why?

Do you think Ben had cause to boast when he rescued Lovon? Why? Why not?

Why do you think he waved aside the praise of the boys when they admired him for saving Lovon?

If there had been any danger when Ben went through the tunnel do you think Ben would still have attempted the rescue? Why?

Do you blame Steven for not going? What do you think you would have done?

6. Maimonides, one of our greatest Jewish teachers, had this to say: "It is best to choose the middle road between haughtiness and humility. A man should know his own worth and respect himself for it. And a man should not humble himself so much that he has no confidence in himself."

Do you agree? Why? Why not?

Why is confidence important if you are to help your fellow man?

What does Steven have to learn according to Maimonides?

Do you think Ben could learn anything from Maimonides? What?

12. MARSHA'S TOPSYTURVY DAY

Marsha searched for her bathing suit on the line behind the cabin. All the other suits were there except hers. "Now I've lost my bathing suit," she announced to her bunkmates when she returned. Everyone helped her look for it but the suit had vanished.

Suddenly Marsha gasped. She had put her ring into the bathing suit pocket for safe keeping when she had gone swimming last Friday. And now it was lost—the gold ring with the shining emerald her grandparents had given to her! What was she going to do?

"Let's post guards east, west, south, and north," cried Susan. "There's a thief in camp!"

Marsha stamped her foot when the girls laughed. "It isn't funny. My gold ring was in the pocket." She bent over her trunk to find another bathing suit. Anger and worry filled every part of her. Suddenly everything had gone wrong. It all began yesterday when she had failed the raft test because of the cramp in her leg. Miriam had warned her not to eat the extra ice-cream but Marsha hadn't listened. Harold had to haul her out of the water. Now, except for Tamar, she was the only one in the bunk who hadn't passed, and Tamar would surely make it soon. And then to make matters worse she had broken the planter she was making for Parents' Visiting Day. The birch-bark log had snapped in her hands while she was scooping out the inside. Now she had to begin all over again, from scratch, and it was hard work.

Tamar had warned her to be careful with the delicate bark but she had been too anxious to be the first to finish. And later she had flared at Tamar when she had flashed her a I-Told-You-So look. Sara had to say, "H.M." to Marsha instead of the other way around. Ann had told Miriam how rude Marsha had been to Tamar, and for the first time that summer, Miriam had to scold her. Marsha scowled at herself and at the bathing suit she took from the trunk. The scolding was still fresh in her mind. "We all fail sometimes," Miriam had said, "and you have to learn to take your failure with the same good cheer you take your success. That's how you grow."

Miriam was right. Marsha knew that. And Tamar was right. Marsha knew that, too.

And now the ring. What was she going to tell her grandparents? And how would she explain it at home? Especially when her mother had warned her not to take the ring to camp. Why had she been so stubborn? Why hadn't she listened?

Her unhappiness grew as the thoughts whirled about in her head.

Miriam tried to chase Marsha's gloom away. "Today is our Oneg Shabbat with Gramps. You know how you've been looking forward to that. How about a smile? A Marsha smile?"

Marsha tried but it was no use. Funny about a smile. If there wasn't one inside you, you couldn't force a real one outside. Even the thought of Gramps whom she loved so much didn't help.

The loss of the ring bothered her. Perhaps she hadn't looked carefully enough! She decided to try again. Carefully she searched deep in the bushes. When she withdrew her head a thorny branch caught at her arm and face, scratching her. In an instant a rush of blood covered her arm. When she touched her face, blood came off on her finger. This was the last straw! What would happen next? She ran to the cabin almost blinded by her tears.

Miriam rushed Marsha to the infirmary. All the girls followed, their faces showing their distress. Miriam told them to wait outside.

Mary went to work. When the last bandage was in place, the nurse patted Marsha's hand and smiled. "There! You'll be as good as new in a jiffy."

When Marsha came out the girls burst out giggling. "You look like a patched-up mummy," laughed Susan, touching the bandage.

Tossing her head, Marsha glared at her bunkmates. She ran back to the cabin, flopped on her bed, and refused to talk. Miriam sighed. The girls sighed. What had happened to Marsha's sunshine? Nobody dared to say a word to her. Marsha had stopped listening.

Tamar blamed herself for Marsha's unhappiness. She tried to apologize. "Look, Marsha, I'm sorry I hurt you. I was only trying to help. You know that."

Marsha's back was stiff. "I'm not even thinking about the planter. Why do you keep harping on that, Tamar? Forget it!" Marsha burrowed her nose into the pillow. She knew that she was making the girls unhappy but she couldn't seem to do a thing about it.

Miriam broke into the silence that followed. Marsha needed another scolding.

"Look Marsha—I know you've been disappointed. We all are sometimes. We have to learn to accept the bad things as well as the good. Do you think you're being fair?"

Marsha looked at Miriam and winked the wetness from her eyes. Her tongue felt dry and no words came.

"Snap out of it!" continued Miriam. "If you dig deep enough I'm sure you'll find something to be happy about. How about it? Will you start digging?"

But Marsha's shovel wasn't working. She rolled over on the bed. "Please, Miriam," she begged, "can't I rest? My arm hurts." She closed her eyes tightly.

Miriam was instantly sorry. "Yes, why don't you rest? Stay in the cabin when we go swimming. By the time we get back, you'll feel more like your old self again." Miriam could see that Marsha was feeling sorry for herself. When Marsha had time to think she'd realize she was wrong. Usually Marsha was sensible. She just needed to be alone.

Soon the cabin was empty. Marsha turned and tossed. She tried to sleep but her unhappiness gave her no rest. She kept hearing Miriam's words. "If we don't fail sometimes, our success doesn't mean anything." What success? She'd never be happy again. Everything and everybody was against her! Her arm throbbed with pain. Perhaps Mary could stop the pain. She ran into the infirmary. Mary patted some salve on the cut and asked her if she wanted to rest there. But Marsha refused.

As she walked along the path, Michael hailed her from the mess hall and came racing toward her. When he spied the bandages he shouted in surprise, "Hey! You've been in a fight! It looks as if the other guy won! Did she pull your hair, too?" Michael examined the top of Marsha's head for a bald spot.

"You think you're funny, don't you?" stormed Marsha. "You don't give a hoot for your only sister! Nobody cares! I wish I were home!"

Michael's bounce unbounced. This was a new twist. He tried to reason with his sister. "A few days ago you said you wished camp would *never* end and today you want to go home. What happened?"

Out poured the long list of woes. Marsha ended with, "Now do you know why I want to go home?"

"Big deal!" laughed Michael. "You're making a mountain out of nothing. Come on—cheer up! The world hasn't come to an end." Michael heaved a sigh of relief. For a while he had thought Marsha really had a problem.

"You're a big help. Remind me never to tell you anything again." Marsha tweaked her brother's nose.

"Oh, boy! Are *you* in a temper! You'd better count to ten. I mean twenty. You're really mad!" Michael laughed at his own advice. Before he could say another word Marsha flounced away. Michael scratched his head. "If I live to be sixty," he shouted after her, "I'll never understand women!"

Back in the cabin Marsha felt confused and lonely. She decided to write to her parents. Suddenly, she wanted them more than anything else in the world. They'd understand. The wrinkles in her forehead deepened as she poured out her trouble on paper. Not for a minute did she stop to think how disturbed Mother and Daddy would be when they read her letter. It was as if Marsha had forgotten that anyone else lived in the world but herself. She addressed the envelope and placed it on her table to mail.

Finally she fell asleep.

* * *

After lunch Emes and S'goolo gathered on Universal Lawn. They sat on the grass waiting for Gramps. Tamar gazed at a flower bed nearby. "Do you suppose that flowers are planted in groups so they won't be lonely, Miriam?" she asked.

"I wouldn't be at all surprised," smiled Miriam. "Flowers are like people. None of us likes to be alone." Miriam glanced at Marsha meaningfully. Marsha's long silence worried her.

Joshua lifted his head toward the slanting rays of the sun. Deep inside himself he said a prayer of thanks to God for his happiness at Kee Tov. The warm feeling of love he felt for all the boys flowed through every part of him.

Bill pointed toward the chapel. Gramps was coming toward

them with a chair in one hand and a package in the other. With a shout of joy the boys leaped to their feet. It was a close race to see who would reach Gramps first to carry his chair. Steven won the honor. Gramps put the package on the grass beside his chair and laughed at all the eager eyes trying to peer into the box.

The Oneg Shabbat discussion began with a question from Miriam. "Gramps," she asked, "in the Talmud the Rabbis asked, 'Who is contented?' And the answer was, 'He who is satisfied with his lot.'" Miriam glanced meaningfully at Marsha, then turned back to Gramps. "What did they mean?"

Gramps followed Miriam's gaze. For the first time he saw Marsha's downcast expression and the bandages on her face and arm. He wondered what had happened, but said nothing.

"First, let me tell you one of my favorite stories," he said, "before we discuss your question, Miriam." Gramps smiled as all the children leaned forward eagerly. "A long time ago there lived a farmer named Jacob. Jacob had a large family. There was Jacob, his wife, and their eight children, all crowded together in one small house. Jacob was discontented with his cramped household. Finally, he could stand it no longer and decided to seek the advice of the rabbi in his village. When the rabbi heard Jacob's complaint, he said, 'Go home, Jacob— and take your cow into the house.'"

Gramps' eyes twinkled when the children giggled.

"Jacob was puzzled but he obeyed. After all, was not his rabbi the wisest man in the village? Now Jacob's household was even more crowded. Things were worse than before. Again he approached the rabbi with more complaints. The rabbi listened patiently. 'Take your horse into the house, Jacob,' he advised. At these words Jacob scratched his head. What kind of advice was this? Still, he didn't dare to disobey his rabbi. He took the horse into his house."

Ben slapped his thighs and rolled over on the grass.

"Now," continued Gramps, "Jacob really had trouble. There

was hardly enough room to move. Again he returned to the rabbi. This time his complaints were louder than ever. 'Take your goat into the house, Jacob,' said the rabbi, calmly.

" 'What!' cried Jacob, looking at the rabbi as if he had lost his mind.

" 'Do as I say,' ordered the rabbi.

"Jacob did as he was told. Now life was impossible. The walls were bulging. Once more Jacob returned. 'Please, Rabbi, I'm almost out of my head. Help me!'

" 'Now,' said the rabbi, 'take all the animals out of your house.'

"Jacob hurried to obey. Soon he returned with a beaming face. 'Rabbi, you are indeed my best friend. Now there is enough room for all of us—more than enough.' "

The surprise ending brought a burst of laughter from the children.

Even Marsha had to smile. But when Miriam caught her eye, the smile vanished. Miriam said to herself, "She's listening anyway. Now, if only Gramps can help."

Gramps waited for the laughter to stop. "And now, Miriam, we come to your question. In Hebrew to be contented with one's lot is called *so-me-ach b'chelko.* The rabbis knew that people who want something too much sometimes break God's rules to get it. So they advised us to accept what we have and go on from there." Gramps looked at Joshua's attentive face. He didn't want to embarrass Joshua by talking about the way he accepted his blindness without complaint. But Joshua was a wonderful example of so-me-ach b'çhelko.

Jeff waved his hand. "Then is it wrong to want something my friend has? I wrote to Dad to send me a camera like Ben's. He wrote that I couldn't have it now. Keeping me at camp was costing too much money this summer. But I still want a camera like Ben's."

"It isn't wrong, Jeff. It's natural to want a camera. But it *will* be wrong if you nag your father to get one. And it would be wrong if you broke a rule to get a camera. What the rabbis meant by so-me-ach b'chelko goes back to the Tenth Commandment, 'Thou shalt not covet!' What does that mean?" Gramps waited for an answer. Susan knew it. "You must not keep thinking about and wanting your neighbor's things. If you keep thinking about it—you might end up by breaking a commandment to try to get it."

Soon the discussion was flying from Ben to Susan, from Ann to Steven, from Michael to Sara, and from Joshua back to Susan. Even Tamar told about the time she wanted the first prize for her painting and was so bitterly disappointed when she didn't win. Their eager voices bumped into each other. Bill, Miriam, and Gramps had to call a halt so that each one would have a turn to talk.

Marsha sat quietly, her eyes glued to her lap. She heard her conscience scolding her. Soon shame began to fill her. Just because a few unpleasant things had happened she had made herself and everyone else miserable. How was she going to straighten out the mess? How was she going to make her bunk believe she was really and truly sorry?

Glancing up she saw the anxious glances Michael kept throwing her way. Instantly she knew what she had to do. Leaping to her feet, she broke into the conversation, and blurted out the words. "Please forgive me, everybody. I'm sorry. Just because things didn't go my way I acted like a spoiled kid!"

As soon as the words popped out of her mouth, Marsha felt better.

At first everyone stared.

But soon the stares changed into understanding smiles. Marsha knew beyond a doubt that her friends had forgiven her. She almost burst with thankfulness.

Gramps had something to say, too. "You were having a bad mood, Marsha. We all have them sometimes." He flashed her an extra special smile. Gramps picked up the the box near his feet and opened it. The children shrieked, "Fudge!" Delicious creamy fudge all wrinkled with nuts!

"And now," Gramps twinkled at the children, "who would like a piece?"

"Who wouldn't?" cried Emes and S'goolo in one voice.

Gramps winked at Bill and Miriam. The box went from hand to hand around the circle.

"What does so-me-ach b'chelko, the contentment we need, lead to?" asked Gramps, when the delicious fudge was almost gone.

"A happy feeling inside yourself," said Marsha, promptly.

"Yes. Another way of saying the same thing, is 'peace.' Peace comes with a happy heart. We love the feeling that flows out of us when we feel good about the good things we do. The Torah teaches us about peace on nearly every page."

Bill had something to add. "The ways of the Torah are ways of pleasantness and all its paths are peace."

Miriam said, "Three things keep the world going—justice, truth, and peace."

Gramps added, "A soft answer turns away anger and increases peace."

Ben yelled, "I'll do anything for *peace* if you'll only give me another *piece* of fudge!" Gramps laughed and gave Ben another piece of fudge.

Bill thought of another story from the Talmud.

"A Rabbi was standing in a busy market-place with the prophet Elijah. They watched many people hurrying about their business. The Rabbi asked Elijah, 'Is there anyone in this great crowd who has really come close to God?'

"Elijah examined each face carefully for a long while. Suddenly, his face lit up with joy. 'Yes, I see two men over there who have truly come close to God.' He pointed to two clowns in ragged clothes who were entertaining a group of people. The Rabbi was astonished when Elijah chose the clowns. 'What makes you give them the honor?'

" 'Because,' smiled Elijah, 'they are merrymakers. When they see people in trouble they do all in their power to cheer them. And when they see two men quarreling, they seek to make peace among them, just as Aaron did in the Bible.' "

Roy came riding along in his jeep with cake and milk for everybody.

After the Oneg Shabbat refreshments Miriam and Bill organized the Israeli folk-dancing.

With a burst of laughter, Marsha took Michael's hand and whirled him around the lawn. Happiness gave wings to her feet. The dance ended with all the children falling to the grass, breathless, rosy, and filled with joy.

*   *   *

When three stars appeared in the sky the camp gathered in the chapel to say good-bye to the Sabbath. Emes was in charge of the Havdolo services. They stood before the altar with shining faces.

Ben held out a wine cup which Steven filled with wine from a pitcher.

"May the coming week be overflowing with the goodness of kind deeds to each other," said Ben. "Blessed art Thou, O Lord, our God, Ruler of the World, who creates the fruit of the vine." Ben sipped the wine.

Joshua lifted a spice-box of polished olive wood. Removing the pointed cover, he inhaled the fragrant spices. "Our beautiful Sabbath has come to a close. May the fragrance of its peace and contentment stay with us during the coming week. Blessed art Thou, O Lord, our God, who creates the different spices."

Michael raised a huge twisted candle with three wicks on the top. The flames merged together into a beautiful torch. Carefully, Michael brought his fingers close to the light, curving them in to cast a shadow. "This shadow I am making," he said, "shows the difference between the light and the darkness. Blessed art Thou, O Lord, our God, who helps us to know the difference between light and darkness, between right and wrong." The flame cast a warm glow on Michael's face.

Jeff dipped the candle flame into the wine cup. The flame sizzled and sputtered out. "Our Sabbath is now over," he announced, "and a new week is beginning. A new week of sharing with each other here at Kee Tov. A new week to show our love for our neighbors."

*　*　*

Later when the lights were out, the girls began their wishing game.

"I wish we had self-lighting books so that we could read in the dark," said Susan who liked to read in bed.

"I wish I could sit on a star and travel all over the world," said Sara, missing her parents.

"I wish I were small enough to swim in a dewdrop," said

Ann, reminding herself to wash her face in dew the next morning.

"I wish they would invent a dishwasher with octopus arms that would scrape, and wash, and dry, and put the dishes away all at the same time," said Tamar who didn't like to do dishes.

"I wish that Kee Tov had lollipop streets, chocolate frosted beds, ice-cream trees, gingerbread porches, cookie walls, and a soda pop lake," laughed Marsha who loved sweets.

"Who is contented?" asked Miriam.

"So-me-ach b'chelko," shouted the girls together.

At that instant, Marsha bolted up in bed, her hand over her mouth. "Miriam! The letter! That terrible letter I wrote to Mother. What will I do? She's going to think I'm dreadfully unhappy at Kee Tov and I'm not!"

"Here it is," laughed Miriam, taking the letter out of her bureau drawer. "When I saw how thick it was, I knew you'd be sorry if I mailed it."

Marsha couldn't tear the letter up fast enough.

She lay in bed wide awake listening to the rain that had begun a steady patter. She thought of the ring she'd lost. It would be hard to tell the family about her carelessness, but she'd have to face it just the same. Tomorrow she'd try to pass the raft test again and start another log planter. This time she'd listen to Tamar and be extra careful.

The last thing she said to herself just before she fell asleep was, "No more topsyturvy living for me. Today just wore me out!"

WHAT DO YOU THINK?

1. Another story that Gramps told the children at the Oneg Shabbat on Universal Lawn came from the Talmud. Rabbi Akiba was traveling on a donkey through the countryside. In one hand he carried his pet rooster and in the other he held a lamp. At nightfall he reached a small town and searched for a place to rest. But no one had any room for him. He was forced to sleep in the woods that surrounded the town.

During the night a wolf killed his donkey, a wildcat ate his rooster, and a strong wind blew out his lamp. Rabbi Akiba said to himself, "Surely all this must be for the good."

In the morning Rabbi Akiba discovered that bandits had attacked the town and carried off the people as captives. He said, "If the donkey had brayed, if the rooster had crowed, or if the bandits had seen my light, I, too, would have been carried off to a strange land to be held captive. *Gam zu l'tovo*—whatever God does is for the best."

Why did Gramps tell this story?

How did Marsha's discontent affect her? How did it affect her bunk?

Do you think Marsha liked herself in the story? How can you tell?

Where was Marsha's thinking wrong? Whom was she blaming? Where did the blame belong?

Do you have days when everything seems to go wrong?

Whose fault is it? Will feeling sorry for yourself help you to accept failure better? How can you help yourself to feel better?

Can you think of a time when you had a disappointment that turned out to be a good thing in the end? Did it happen at home or at school or at play? What did you do about it? When you accept disappointment, how do you feel? When you don't, how do you feel? How do your actions affect the people around you? Does anyone give you advice as Miriam gave Marsha?

Do you agree with Miriam when she said, "If you dig deep enough you can always find something to be happy about"? Why? Why not?

2. Gramps called being contented with one's lot, so-me-ach b'chelko.

Does this mean that you are to sit back and take it easy while you're waiting for something to happen? Give your reasons for your answer.

Can you think of a time when you were not contented with what you had and kept wanting what your friend had, too? Did this bring contentment to you? Did your actions make the people around you happy?

What can Joshua teach us about so-me-ach b'chelko?

If you are not so-me-ach b'chelko, you keep thinking about and wanting your neighbor's things. This is breaking the Tenth Commandment.

How can breaking this commandment lead to unhappiness?

Can you think of a time when you or a friend did something wrong in order to get what another friend had? What happened?

The Rabbis in the Talmud also said, "Envy has a thousand eyes, and not one is right." When the Rabbis said this they tried to teach people that envy might lead to jealousy, and jealousy might lead to hate. Hate, they warned, made people harm themselves and others.

Do you agree with them? Why? Why not?

Have you ever found yourself hating someone who had something you wanted? What happened?

God wants us to work hard to reach our goals. When you reach a goal you have set for yourselves and find that your friend has more than you, then, said the Rabbis, it would be wise to accept your lot and go on from there.

How can this advice help you at home? At school? At play? With your neighbor?

3. In the Bible we read that Moses met discontent many times as he led the people in the wilderness after they left Egypt.

The people weren't used to desert life and desert hardships. First they complained about the bitterness of the drinking water. God helped Moses to sweeten the water. Then they complained about the food. God helped Moses by sending manna for them to eat. When Moses was away for forty days on Mt. Sinai receiving the Law, the people grew discontented again and built the Golden Calf to worship.

Nevertheless, Moses pleaded with God to forgive the people for their sins of discontent. He knew that it would take a long time for a slave people to get used to freedom.

What kind of a leader did Moses have to be in order to make his people happy?

Could Moses think of his own happiness while this was going on?

How did Moses live "Thou shalt love thy neighbor as thyself"?

How did Moses live so-me-ach b'chelko?

How did he live Kee Tov?

How did he live Emes B'libo?

What can this story teach us about our life today?

How are we different from the people Moses led out of Egypt?

How can we learn from their mistakes today?

4. The Rabbis in the Midrash tell us that Aaron, Moses' brother, loved peace. They say that he loved men and helped them to know God. He turned away from no man. His kindness led sinners to do good. When a sinner was about to do something wrong, he would stop and say to himself, "How shall I face Aaron who has been so kind to me?" And the sinner would not do the wrong.

When Aaron discovered that two men had quarreled, he would hurry to each of them at different times. To the first man he would say, "My son, do you know how unhappy you are making the man whom you believe to be your enemy? I have just seen him. His heart is heavy with sadness and he cried out to me, 'I have sinned against my neighbor. I cannot bear to face him after what I have done to him!' "

Then Aaron would hurry to the second man and repeat the very same thing. When the two men met they would become friends once more.

How did Aaron obey God's law, "Love peace and pursue it"?

How did Gramps' story about Elijah follow God's law of peace?

Can you think of a time when you or a friend were peacemakers like Aaron? How did you feel? What good did you do?

How did Gramps connect contentment with peace? Do you agree? Why?

The Nobel Prize is given each year to the person who does the best work for world peace. Appoint several members in your class to find out about the Nobel Peace Prize winners of past years. Read the reports to the class. Discuss the ways in which these peacemakers helped to prove that the laws of the

Torah "are ways of pleasantness and all her paths are peace."

5. The Talmud has a story about Rabbi Meir. One Friday night he was preaching a sermon in the synagogue. Among those who came to listen was a woman. After the sermon, the woman stayed to hear the discussion. By the time she arrived home it was very late. The angry husband refused to let her come into the house. "You cannot come home," he raged, "until you spit into Rabbi Meir's face."

The woman, of course, would not insult her beloved rabbi in this way.

Rabbi Meir heard about the affair and sent for the woman.

"I have a pain here," he said, pointing to his eye, "can you cure it?"

The woman stared at the rabbi. "How can I, a poor ignorant woman, cure the great rabbi's eye?"

"Do as I ask. Spit into my eye seven times. I know you can help me."

The woman did as she was told. Rabbi Meir laughed. "Now return to your husband and tell him that you have spit in Rabbi Meir's eye, not once, but seven times."

When his pupils heard what their rabbi had done they asked how he could allow himself to be so insulted.

"I would do anything to bring peace between a man and his wife," said the rabbi.

How was Rabbi Meir like Aaron?

What sentences in the Havdolo service would have pleased Aaron and Rabbi Meir?

6. Ruth was in Marsha's class at the Lawrence School. She was the smartest girl in the class. Everything she did was almost perfect. One Monday, to her great surprise, she got back a test paper and found two arithmetic problems marked wrong. Instead of the usual 100 she was given a 60. Ruth burst into tears and cried and cried over her failure. On Tuesday the same thing happened. When the same thing happened on Wednesday, too, the teacher sent for

Ruth's mother. Ruth's mother said, "Ruth acts like this all the time. She can't bear failure. She takes after me. She wants to be perfect."

If you had been the teacher what would you have said to Ruth's mother?

Do you like what Ruth's mother said? Why?

Does your mother feel the same way Ruth's mother does?

Have you ever had an experience like this? Tell us about it.

What might Rabbi Akiba say to Ruth? What might Aaron say to Ruth? What might Moses say?

Do you think that Ruth's unhappiness had anything to do with her failure?

Let's pretend that we are present when the teacher talks to Ruth and her mother. One child can be the teacher and say what she thinks the teacher might have said. Another child can be Ruth, and a third child can be her mother. Say what you feel. Let two boys be Aaron and Rabbi Meir. Try to use some of the quotations we have used from the Bible and the Talmud.

13. HAVE MERCY!

The girls were returning from a nature trip. Walking five abreast, they sang a marching song, matching their steps to the music. Miriam walked at the end of the line.

Just as they were passing a white farmhouse, a little girl about five years old ran out the door, screaming. She raced over to the fence with tears rolling down her cheeks. "My mommy! My mommy! She fell on the floor and she won't wake up!" Her streaming eyes pleaded for help.

Miriam and the girls rushed into the farmhouse. Inside they found a woman stretched out on the kitchen floor, her eyes closed, her face white. Miriam felt the woman's pulse. "Get me some water quickly," said Miriam, without looking up. Tamar brought the water.

Miriam put a few drops of water on the woman's lips. After a few seconds she opened her eyes. Moaning weakly, she clutched her right side and stared up at the anxious faces. When the child saw her mother awaken, she knelt to hug her. "Mommy, are you better now? I was scared when you fell down. You wouldn't speak to me." The child burst into fresh tears.

"Don't worry, Laurie darling," comforted her mother. "Now that we have help, everything will be all right." The woman tried to smile, but again the pain stabbed at her. She closed her eyes.

"We'd better get a doctor right away," said Miriam. "Do you have a phone?" The woman pointed to a phone in the hall. "I guess I fainted," she explained. "I don't know what to do. My husband won't be home until tonight. He's away on a cattle-buying trip. This pain may be appendix trouble. I've had attacks like it before. I'm Mrs. McDonald." Her voice sounded tired.

"Let's see what the doctor says," said Miriam, helping Mrs. McDonald to her feet and leading her to a bedroom off the kitchen. Laurie followed them, hanging on to her mother's skirt.

The girls looked at the dishes piled in the sink. It was easy to see that Mrs. McDonald had been too ill to do her chores that morning.

"Let's clean the kitchen," suggested Sara. They decided to wait until Miriam came out before they tackled the job. Miriam telephoned the doctor who promised to come quickly. When she hung up the phone, the girls asked her if they could clean the kitchen. Miriam was pleased with their thoughtfulness. "That's a wonderful idea. I'm going to stay in the bedroom with Mrs. McDonald. She's very upset and worried. Divide the work among you. You'll have to take care of Laurie, too. Her mother needs to rest."

When Laurie came out of the bedroom the girls made a big fuss over her. Soon they had her smiling and chattering. Susan sat her in a chair and gave her a cookie. Sara cleared the table. Ann washed the dishes and Marsha and Susan wiped. Tamar swept the floor. They worked quickly and quietly. By the time the doctor arrived, the kitchen sparkled. They took Laurie out on the porch and played with her to keep her from thinking of her sick mother. Laurie showed them her dolls and her doll house. Soon they all were playing house.

Miriam came out with the doctor. "It's a good thing for Mrs. McDonald that you came along when you did," said the doctor to Miriam, "I don't even want to think of what might have happened. I'll have to drive Mrs. McDonald to the hospital right away. That appendix has to come out. There's no time to lose. I'll phone Mr. McDonald and tell him everything."

"Is there anything more we can do?" asked Miriam.

A worried frown appeared on the doctor's forehead. "It's Laurie—I'm worried about her. My wife is away or we'd care for her until her daddy comes home. Mrs. McDonald won't go to the hospital unless Laurie is left with some very responsible people."

"Let me call Kee Tov and ask Mr. Green, my director, if we can help!"

Aaron didn't hesitate for a minute. "Bring Laurie back to Kee Tov. We'll be glad to help."

When Mrs. McDonald heard that Laurie would be safe at Kee Tov, she felt better right away. "How can I ever thank you and the girls enough?" she said with a thankful smile. "I'll never forget your kindness."

Miriam waved Mrs. McDonald's thanks away. "It was no trouble at all. I'm sure you would have done the same if it had been the other way 'round."

Mrs. McDonald kissed Laurie. She told her to be a good girl and obey her new friends.

The doctor bundled his patient into the car and quickly rode away.

Tamar took Laurie's right hand and Susan took her left. Sara and Marsha and Ann hovered nearby like mother hens. Miriam could see that Laurie was going to get plenty of attention from her five new-found mothers. With a wide grin, Miriam brought up the rear, pleased with the way her girls had handled this sudden problem.

It didn't take long for Laurie to feel as if she had been at Kee Tov for a long time. At lunch, Aaron introduced the new guest. He stood Laurie on a chair so that everybody could see her. Laurie laughed until her cheeks were rosy when the campers made up a cheer just for her.

BICKERY, BOCKERY, BOO,
A KEE TOV WELCOME, DEAR LAURIE, FOR YOU!

Aaron hugged the happy child and Laurie gave him a butterfly kiss right on the tip of his nose to the delight of everyone in the dining hall. Another cheer followed quickly.

EENIE, MEENIE, MINIE, MOSE,
CATCH THAT KISS ON AARON'S NOSE.

Joe gave Laurie a treat he had baked especially for her. Laurie clapped with excitement. Into her hand slipped a fat gingerbread man with raisin eyes, raisin nose, and a raisin mouth. On its head Joe had fashioned a frosted pink hat. Laurie hugged the gingerbread man to her chest, refusing to eat it. She asked Miriam to save the gingerbread man for her so she could show it to her parents.

After lunch, something happened that kept the girls in S'goolo busy all during rest hour. It began when Tamar was changing from her hiking shoes to her sneakers. As she slipped her foot into the right sneaker, she screamed, "There's a spider in my sneaker!" Tamar held the sneaker away from her body, dangling it by the string.

But it wasn't a spider at all. The long legs Tamar thought belonged to a spider turned out to be the long, thread-like tails of five baby white-footed mice. Somehow, the mother had crept into Tamar's sneaker and had given birth to her babies. The girls crowded around Tamar, their eyes wide as saucers. Never had they seen such tiny animals. Susan dumped a box of note-

paper on her bed and they carefully placed the babies in the empty box.

The babies scurried to a corner. Huddling together they sought each other's warmth, their bodies trembling.

"Where's the mother deermouse?" asked Marsha. "These babies have to have milk. They'll die if they don't get it."

"What a pity," said Ann. "They're so darling."

"Let's put our pity to work and do something about it," said Miriam.

The problem was a hard one. How were they going to feed the helpless babies?

Sara suggested a baby bottle but they vetoed that idea. The babies were too tiny. Susan thought of a straw but they abandoned that idea, too. The babies wouldn't know what to do with a straw. Miriam finally came up with the best suggestion. An eye dropper! Of course! Just the thing! Ann ran for warm milk and Tamar for the dropper. But when they tried to feed the deermice, they refused the milk.

What could they do? The deermice would surely die soon if they were not fed!

While they were tossing the problem around, Laurie bent over the box and fondly gazed at the babies. Picking up the medicine dropper, she dipped it into the milk just as she had seen her mother do when she put drops into the eyes of a newborn calf. Placing the dropper close to one baby's mouth she squeezed a tiny drop. The mouth twitched and the milk fell on Laurie's finger instead. Before she could snatch her finger away the baby deermouse was climbing all over her finger sucking the milk with a happy squeak.

"Look! Look! The baby is drinking my finger!" Laurie dropped some more milk on her finger and gave it to another baby. Soon the deermice were clinging to all her fingers, sucking the milk greedily.

"Of course," explained Miriam, "they didn't like the hard

glass of the eye dropper. Laurie's finger was more like their mother's body."

Soon all the girls were dipping their fingers into the milk and feeding the hungry babies. They decided to take turns with the feeding all that day. Miriam posted a meal schedule on the wall. Laurie wanted her name on the list, too. The girls hugged her for helping them solve their problem.

"In a few days," said Miriam, "we can try some other foods to see what they like best. Tomorrow I think it would be better to bring them to the science museum so that the rest of Kee Tov can enjoy them and watch them grow, too."

"I wonder if the mother will come back," said Marsha.

"We'll be their mother," grinned Susan, giving Laurie another hug.

"Just as God is merciful, so are you merciful," said Miriam, looking proudly at her girls.

Later that same day, Jeff found a brown thrasher dragging its wing on the ground. Rushing into the cabin, he cried, "Look what I found! I think its wing is broken."

The boys crowded around Jeff.

"Looks to me like it's dying," said Michael.

Jeff looked at the bird trembling in his hand and stroked its head gently. The thrasher didn't have enough strength to lift its head. It lay quietly, looking at Jeff with helpless eyes.

"Can't we do anything about it?" Jeff asked. "We can't let it die!"

"Let's ask Mary," suggested Steven. "She knows all about First Aid. I bet she'll be able to help."

Mary could—and she did.

The boys watched her swift, sure fingers make a small splint. Gently, she bandaged the broken wing close to the thrasher's body.

Now another problem presented itself. When Jeff tried to feed it some bread crumbs, the bird wouldn't open its beak. Mary tried. No success, either!

A worried feeling began to grow inside Jeff. "For all we know, the bird may have been hurt for a long time before I found it," he said, feeling as if the bird were his special responsibility. In that short time, he had become closely attached to the bird. He had to do something—and quickly! He appealed to the group around him. "There must be something we can do! Let's circle our ideas in orbit. Six heads ought to come up with something!"

Soon the boys were arguing.

"Maybe the thrasher doesn't like bread," said Ben. "How about a different food?"

"Let's try worms," said Michael. "I'll dig some up in a jiffy."

"But it's too weak to tackle worms," objected Joshua. "Let's ask Joe for something."

"Let's get a bird book from the science library," said Steven, "and see if we can get any information there."

The argument grew more and more heated. Everyone talked at once.

Jeff was quiet. He shook his head. A feeling of discouragement took hold of him. He gazed at the thrasher's still body. Its life seemed to be slipping away before his eyes. Nothing they were saying had anything to do with the problem at hand.

"I don't think the kind of food we give the bird matters at all," he said, breaking into the argument. "We have to think of a way to get the food down the bird's throat."

"Why can't we just open its beak and force the food down?" asked Steven.

"That's a good question," said Jeff, impatiently, "but how do we do it?"

Mary's face brightened and she snapped her fingers. "I've thought of something—here's hoping my idea works!"

When she told the boys, they thought her idea was worth trying.

Jeff soaked some bread in water until it was soggy. He gently forced open the bird's beak while Mary pushed the soft wet bread down the thrasher's throat with a pair of tweezers. The bread slipped down smoothly.

Everyone breathed a deep sigh of relief when they saw the bird try to flutter its good wing a short time later. Slowly, its dull eyes began to shine. Little by little, life began to return to its tiny body. It was like a miracle.

Jeff danced around Mary. "You're a genius, Mary!" he shouted. His joy made his spine tingle.

"Think nothing of it," laughed Mary, "part of the day's work!"

She fixed a bed of soft cotton in a bureau drawer and placed the bird on it.

"Your bird will be as good as new in a few days," she promised.

Jeff knelt down to peer closely at the bird again. With a feeble chirp the bird pecked at a strand of Jeff's curly hair. Then, tucking its head under its good wing, it went to sleep. Jeff beamed.

The infirmary door slammed and Bill came in. "Oh, here you are!" he said to the boys. "I was beginning to think you'd gone off on a rocket trip to the moon. What are you all doing here?"

All the boys began to talk at once. Bill flung his hands up in the air and closed his eyes. "Time out!" he shouted. "One at a time, please!"

Jeff told the story with help from Steven, Michael, Joshua, and Ben. Even Mary remembered something they'd forgotten to mention.

Bill looked at the thrasher and smiled, "Which reminds me of a story."

Sitting on the infirmary beds the boys listened.

"A Chasidic Rabbi was wandering about a country fair in Poland long ago. He noticed some calves standing in the hot sun, their tongues hanging out from thirst. Flies, swarming on their hot, wet backs, added to their misery. The Rabbi knew at once that the owners had gone away without remembering to care for their beasts. Quickly, he filled many buckets with water and soon made the calves cool and comfortable.

"One of the owners returned with some more calves. Mistaking the Rabbi for a hired hand, he commanded the Rabbi to water the new calves. The Rabbi obeyed without a word. But when the dealer offered him money the Rabbi refused.

"'I cannot take your money,' he said. 'I did not water the calves because you ordered me to do it. I obeyed God's commandment which says, "Be merciful to all My creatures."'"

Just as Bill's story came to an end the thrasher lifted its head and chirped.

"See!" said Jeff, twinkling up at Bill. "The thrasher likes good stories, too!" Bill threw back his head and roared.

"The Rabbis in the Talmud called an act of mercy towards helpless animals, 'Tzar Ba-ale Chayim.' I know they would have liked the way you helped the thrasher back to life."

This time the thrasher trilled a longer song than before.

"Tzar Ba-ale Chayim," said Bill, again.

WHAT DO YOU THINK?

1. The Hebrew phrase reminding us, "Be merciful to all My creatures," is known as Tzar Ba-ale Chayim.

   List all the ways Emes and S'goolo obeyed God's commandment to practice Tzar Ba-ale Chayim.

   When you have pets at home what is your responsibility toward them?

   Can you tell about a time when you saw a neighbor not practicing Tzar Ba-ale Chayim? What did you do?

The Rabbis in the Talmud were concerned in many ways about how animals should be treated. What they said long ago holds true for us today. They said: "No man may buy an animal until he has provided for it."

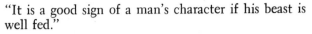

"It is a good sign of a man's character if his beast is well fed."

"A master should feed his animal before he feeds himself."

Can these rules help us to care for our pets today? How?

Look up the activities of the Animal Rescue League or the Society for the Prevention of Cruelty to Animals in your community and report to your class about them.

How do these organizations obey the mitzvah of Tzar Ba-ale Chayim?

2. Sometimes Michael and Marsha forget to feed their parakeet. They get so interested in their other activities, they forget about their pet. One day Daddy put his foot down. "If you don't take care of your pet every day on time, I'm going to give him away to someone who *will* care for him properly."

Do you think Mr. Ross was too harsh with the twins? Why?

What quotations from the Talmud did the twins have to learn?

3. Pity is the sadness you feel when you see suffering. Mercy is the sadness you feel when you see suffering *plus* the good deed of doing something about it.

What did Miriam say that shows she knew the difference between pity and mercy?

How did the boys change their pity into mercy?

Can you think of a time when something happened to you or to your friend where pity turned into mercy?

Miriam told the girls this legend from the Midrash. The Rabbis used it to explain the mitzvah, "You shall be merciful, just as God is merciful."

When the Israelites finally crossed the Red Sea, they sang and danced their praises of thanks to God. The angels in heaven wanted to sing and dance, too. But God would not allow it. God, the Rabbis said, silenced His angels with, "The Egyptians are My children, too. Yet you wish to sing Me a song of praise while they drown in the sea."

Does this show how the Rabbis believed God loves all people? How?

4. When Mr. McDonald came to get Laurie he was grateful to Kee Tov for their hospitality to Laurie. Laurie showed him the mice and told him all about the problem S'goolo had had with the feeding. It reminded him of a true story.

"When I was getting ready for my spring plowing," he said, "I took my jeep out of the barn. When I was hooking it to the plow, I discovered a nest in the back of the jeep. On the nest was a mother hen warming her eggs. When I tried to remove the hen, she squawked so loudly that I decided to let her stay. Every day I fed her grain and water, and every day she bumped along with me while I was plowing. And I can tell you she was really jolted around quite a bit!

"When her eggs were hatched, the hen broadcast the news to the whole farmyard. Then she took her chicks out, one by one, and carried them to the barnyard." Mr. McDonald's eyes twinkled. "Do you think the chicks said, 'Cheep, cheep,' or do you think they said, 'Jeep, Jeep'?"

How did Mr. McDonald obey the commandment in the Bible that says, "You shall not take a mother bird away from her young"?

Can you find the place in Chapter 9 where this same commandment was carried out?

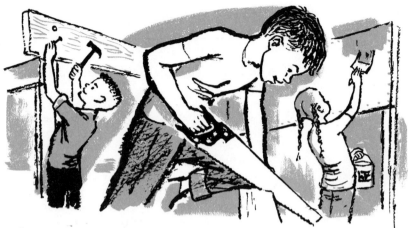

14. TOMBOLA

"When I see my mother and daddy this afternoon," Susan said to Sara, "I'm going to hug and kiss them to pieces. It seems like a year and half since I've seen them." Susan danced around Sara in a gay whirl.

The girls and Miriam were on their way to the plant nursery carrying their log planters. Gramps was going to show them how to plant geraniums.

Sara smiled at Susan's enthusiasm, but the smile stopped at her eyes. Quick tears welled up and she ran ahead without answering. She didn't want the girls to see her cry.

"What's the matter with her?" asked Susan, lifting her eyebrows. "She's been acting funny all day, hardly saying a word to anyone."

"She has?" asked Miriam. "I hadn't noticed." Miriam's eyes followed Sara. For the first time she noticed the sad droop of her shoulders. "Did Sara say anything that might give us a clue to what's troubling her?" Miriam asked.

"She did tell me yesterday that she wished her parents were

home from Europe," recalled Marsha. "She said she missed them terribly."

Now S'goolo knew exactly what was troubling Sara. No doubt about it! Sara would be the only one without visitors that afternoon. The girls gazed with sympathetic eyes at Sara's back. Her problem became theirs. They walked slowly along the path—thinking.

Marsha thought of her mother's last letter. Not only were her own parents coming but her grandparents, too. All at once Marsha knew the answer. She chuckled gaily. "My grandparents are coming, too. Why can't they be Sara's make-believe parents this afternoon?"

"What a dandy idea, Marsha," cried Susan. "Will your grandparents be willing?"

"They're always doing things for people. When I tell them how unhappy Sara is, they'll help. I know they will."

The S'goolo blues disappeared. The girls looked with admiration at Marsha's shining face. They knew she would convince her grandparents to help Sara.

"That's the real spirit of ts'doko, Marsha—lending your grandparents to Sara with lovingkindness," said Miriam, smiling. "Let's not tell Sara until you talk to your family. It'll be a grand surprise."

Deep excitement filled Marsha. So many good things were going to happen today. First—her family was coming, and then the Tombola. Marsha smiled to herself when she remembered how it had happened.

A few weeks ago Miriam had received a letter from her sister in Israel. In it she told about a children's village she had visited named "Shelanu," and she described the new gymnasium in the village. Unfortunately, there had not been enough money left, after the building was completed, to buy the gym equipment the children needed. When Miriam finished reading the letter to the girls, she said, "What good is a gym without equipment?"

"Does that mean that the children haven't any balls and tennis nets the way we have here at Kee Tov?" Susan asked.

"How awful," Ann said. "Can't we do something about it?"

Then and there the idea had been born. Why couldn't Kee Tov earn enough money to buy the equipment for the new gym at Shelanu?

Susan suggested the idea to the camp council and the delegates voted to make it a Kee Tov project. Aaron placed a huge barrel outside the dining hall marked, "Idea Barrel." Into it the campers dropped their suggestions. When a vote was taken, the idea of a carnival, or Tombola, won.

Each bunk was responsible for one booth. What would be sold at the booth had to be decided by the bunk itself. The campers wrote letters to their parents explaining the project. Everyone asked his parents to bring something that could be sold or auctioned. A special committee asked the people who did business with Kee Tov to donate gifts, too.

Kee Tov became a beehive of activity. Hammers pounded, nails banged, paint splashed, saws buzzed. Overnight, the wide path along the lake was changed into a midway, lined with blue and white booths.

Excitement mounted each day as the Tombola and the visiting day drew nearer. Kee Tov bent cheerfully and willingly to the giant task. And now they were ready for the big day.

At the chapel the girls found Gramps waiting. Beside him was a neat pile of geraniums with plump roots dangling from their stems. With his help they set to work.

Tamar patted the soil around a flower. "Wasn't it a wonderful surprise when Aaron gave a Torah for ts'doko to every bunk last Friday?" she asked Gramps. The girls laughed. Aaron had announced the award with, "Each one of you has given your time, energy, and love to our Kee Tov project. And each of you has worked with your whole heart." Then, with a big grin, Aaron had shouted, "To Kee Tov—for true ts'doko!"

Gramps smiled at the happy faces around him. "I heard

those cheers. They almost blasted the flagpole from the ground."

Ann said, "Gramps, I've been wondering about something. Why is the Hebrew word for charity called 'ts'doko' when it really means 'justice'?"

"A good question, Ann," replied Gramps with a smile. "The answer can be found in our Torah. There it tells us how we must give ts'doko—so that it is just. In ancient days, the owner of a field or a vineyard was commanded by God to share his harvest with the poor who lived in his neighborhood. If any grain fell to the ground as the reaper was gathering the barley, he had to leave it for the hungry. If grain was forgotten in the fields, the owner couldn't return to pick it up, either. He had to leave it for the poor. Neither could he choose the people to whom to give his gifts. Anyone in need had the right to come into the field."

"That's like the story of Ruth and Naomi," recalled Tamar. "Ruth gleaned in the field of Boaz because she and Naomi were hungry."

"That's exactly why ts'doko means justice, Tamar," explained Gramps. "The laws of the Torah were for everyone. Ruth came from a strange land—she was not born a Jew. Yet the Jews helped Ruth, the stranger, just as they helped their own people. They knew that God's laws for the poor were just, and they knew that when they practiced the mitzvah of ts'doko, they were God's partners."

"It seems strange for us to be helping the children of Shelanu when we don't even know them," said Susan, snipping a dry leaf off her geranium.

"The State of Israel didn't know these children when they came from the four corners of the world. The Israelis had to give up many things so that these children could be cared for properly. One of the first things Israel promised when it became a nation was that any Jew who wanted and needed a home would be welcome. This is ts'doko—helping strangers to be free once more in a land of their own so that they can say, 'This is my own country. Now I belong.' "

Gramps looked up to see that the girls had lined up their planters on the chapel balcony like bright soldiers on parade.

"How much are you charging for the beautiful planters, girls?" he asked.

"Two dollars each," cried S'goolo in one voice.

"That doesn't seem like much, does it?" said Ann. "We need so much equipment for Shelanu." She wrinkled her freckled nose at Gramps. He patted Ann's sleeve. "The Talmud tells us that each thread in a blouse joins another thread to form the cloth. So, too, every bit of money joins with the rest of the money to form a larger sum. Besides, ts'doko isn't measured just by how much you give. It's measured just as much by what the giving means to you."

"That's what my religious school teacher says," said Marsha. "When we bring our Keren Ami every week, it soon adds up to a large sum. Then we can help many people who need it."

After lunch, the twins watched the road. The minutes seemed like hours as they waited for their first glimpse of the family car.

"Michael," said Marsha, "Laurie's grandmother baked ten blueberry pies for us to sell with our planters. When she heard about the children at Shelanu, she said she wanted to help, too."

"Mr. McDonald wanted to help, too. He gave us ten rabbits to sell," announced Michael. "I helped him unload them before lunch."

Michael saw the car approaching.

"There they are!" he yelled out, dragging Marsha forward. He yanked so hard, her pony tail flew up in the air.

Everyone spoke at once. Nobody knew what anyone else was saying.

Marsha lost no time asking her grandparents to help Sara. They agreed immediately. They hurried over to Sara who was standing forlornly beside Miriam. She was clutching Miriam's hand to keep from feeling so lonely.

Marsha introduced her grandparents to Sara. Grandfather bowed low. "May we have the honor of being your parents for the day?" he asked.

"We know we can't take the place of your real parents, but we'd like to try, Sara," added Grandmother with a friendly smile.

The quick flash of joy that lit up Sara's face made Grandmother and Grandfather bend down and give Sara a hug and a kiss—and a big box of cookies. Sara looked gratefully at Marsha. "Thanks, Marsha, for lending me your grandparents. I'll take good care of them, I promise."

The air was filled with the sound of excited voices, as introductions flew around. The twins couldn't stop talking. There was so much to tell! Mrs. Ross kept interrupting Mr. Ross, who kept interrupting the twins, who kept interrupting each other.

The Tree of Life was one of the main attractions. Streams of parents examined the glowing branches as their children proudly pointed to their Torahs.

The carnival spirit of Tombola livened the midway. Parents crowded along the path. They stopped—they examined—they bought. The money began to roll into Kee Tov faster than a roller coaster.

S'goolo's planters were all sold quickly. The delicious odor of Mrs. McDonald's blueberry pies attracted the mothers like a magnet. No sales talk was needed. The pies sold themselves!

Marsha joined her parents, urging them to buy and buy and buy. She was delighted when they bought a birch-bark mail-box and two birch-bark notebook covers for the twins when they went back to school. Grandmother bought two pine cone Sabbath candle holders and a basket woven of black ash splints.

They stopped at the Emes booth. Michael's voice boomed out into the crowd, "See them hop! See them run! Step right up, ladies and gentlemen!"

Jeff chimed in after Michael with, "Only a few left! One and only one to a customer!"

Joshua added, "Guaranteed to hop right into your hearts!"

Marsha urged her parents on to another booth—there was so much for them to see—and buy, she hoped.

Shortly afterwards, Ben and Steven came running up to the Emes booth, their faces flushed with excitement. "What do you think?" Steven said to Michael. "One father saw our bird-houses and he wants to buy all of them for his gift shop!"

"He says he can sell them easily," added Ben. "And he wants to give us ten dollars for all five of them."

"Of course," said Michael with a big grin, "anything for Shelanu!"

"Ditto!" agreed Joshua. "What a wonderful break!"

Jeff turned pale. Sell *his* bird-house! He saw his plans for the winter sink down like a flat tire. He had looked forward to the fun he would have watching the habits of the winter birds in his back yard. And there wasn't enough time left to make another bird-house. He bit his lower lip stubbornly. Why did that man have to pick the bird-houses? Why couldn't he have chosen something else? No—he wouldn't sell his bird-house! He knew the boys wouldn't like what he was going to say, but he said it, anyway.

"I don't want to sell my bird-house," Jeff announced, firmly. Once the words had left his mouth, Jeff didn't dare to look at his friends. Instead, he examined the tail of a rabbit in a cage.

The boys were speechless.

Steven was the first to speak. "But, Jeff," he tried saying in a convincing tone, "we're all working on this together. If you hold back, the man won't buy any. He wants all five."

Jeff didn't answer. He knew he was being selfish but he was determined to keep his bird-house, come what may. At that moment, he remembered the Torah of ts'doko everyone at Kee Tov had earned. He shook his head, torn between doing what he knew was right and what he really wanted to do.

"Why don't you want to sell it?" asked Joshua.

Jeff explained about his winter project, ending with, "There isn't time to make another bird-house." He hoped they'd understand that he wasn't being mean about the whole affair. He wanted to help Shelanu, he really did, but not with his only bird-house.

"How would it be," suggested Michael, "if we all pitched in and helped you make another one? With five of us working together, we could whip it up in short order. Maybe it won't be as good as yours, but the birds won't care if it isn't so fancy. All they really want is the good food you put into the bird-house." Michael laughed at his own joke.

Michael made good sense to Jeff. Leave it to Michael! He always had a good solution. "All right!" he agreed, lowering his eyes and suddenly very much ashamed of his selfishness. "I'm sorry I made such a fuss."

Ben and Steven raced away with the good news. "More money for Shelanu's equipment!" Steven shouted as he ran down the midway.

"Thanks, Michael," said Jeff, "I guess I wasn't a good sport, was I? Are you going to tell Bill?" A worried frown puckered his forehead.

"Why tell Bill? It was your bird-house. I don't always want to give my things away, either. Sometimes it's hard to do the right thing even though you know you ought to."

Just then, the loudspeaker blasted out the announcement of the auctions. Aaron was the first auctioneer. Quickly he sold all the donated gifts. The crowd cheered when they saw the next auctioneer step up on the platform next to Aaron. It was Gramps. When everyone was quiet, he stepped forward. "The Talmud says," he began with his special smile, " 'A man may give little, but because his heart goes with it, his deed and himself are blessed.' " Gramps paused to take a breath. "Our director at Kee Tov wants to give away a small part of his face. His willingness to part with his pride and joy makes himself and his deed blessed. The highest bidder will have the pleasure of shaving off Aaron's mustache." Gramps laughed at the astonished audience. "Who will be the first to bid—for Shelanu?" he asked, pointing to Aaron's mustache.

Kee Tov was ready with a cheer they had written for this part of the Tombola:

> SNISHERY, SNOSHERY, SNASH,
>
> OPEN YOUR WALLETS,
>
> GET OUT YOUR CASH.
>
> HIGHEST BIDDER
>
> SHAVES AARON'S MUSTACHE.

The bids came fast and furiously. Up—up—they climbed. Each camper tried to get his parents to bid higher and higher.

"Twelve dollars!" shouted one Na-arim father.

"Do I hear more?" asked Gramps, pleading for someone to say more.

Aaron stroked his mustache lovingly. He held the razor out toward the audience, begging them to raise their bids.

"Twelve once—twelve twice," Gramps slowly called the numbers and rolled his eyes at the audience.

"Twenty-five dollars!" shouted a voice from the back. Everyone turned to see Ben's father striding forward with long steps. Holding his hand was Ben, grinning broadly.

No one bid higher. Ben's father had a wonderful time. He mixed the lather and first, he dabbed Aaron's forehead, then his cheeks, and then the tip of his nose.

"I'm sacrificing my mustache, not my face," shouted Aaron, above the roaring laughter of the crowd.

A big blob of lather went dashing onto Aaron's mustache. Ben's father went into his act like a circus clown. He scared Aaron nearly out of his wits, but he finally finished the job with swift, sure strokes.

"Aaron's face looks bald," giggled Marsha.

The next auctioneer was Matt Johnson. Holding a baseball

out to the audience, he said, "This ball has been autographed by every player of the mighty Giant team. Who'll start the bidding with ten dollars? For Shelanu!"

All the fathers drooled. All the sons drooled. Some of the girl baseball fans drooled, too. Matt read the names on the baseball slowly and clearly in his deep voice. The audience went wild. In ten minutes, the ball was sold for seventeen dollars.

Matt grinned from ear to ear when the children shouted a cheer especially for him:

> HIT THAT BASEBALL,
>
> CRACK THAT BAT,
>
> KEE TOV LOVES HIM,
>
> HE'S OUR MATT!

The counselors did their share of ts'doko, too.

Bill permitted the campers to throw wet sponges at him for ten cents a throw. A long line of children kept him ducking for half an hour.

Esther allowed a father to cut off her pony tail for five dollars.

Roy sat on a chair under a tree. Above his head was a gallon bucket of water. As soon as the campers collected twenty-five dollars, Bill gave a signal to Ben and Jeff waiting in the tree. With all their might the boys jerked the cord. Down came the water drenching Roy. He shook off the water and roared at the crowd good-naturedly.

Even Joe got into the act. He gave all the Y'lodim a ride on his back up and down the midway for ten cents a ride. Michael had the first ride. As he climbed off Joe's back, he said, "Don't strain yourself, Joe. We wouldn't want to miss your wonderful cooking."

At five o'clock the Tombola was over. There was no doubt about its success. Now they would be able to send a good part of the needed equipment to Shelanu.

The parents prepared to leave. Marsha and Michael watched

their family get into the car. Their merriment vanished for a moment as they said good-bye.

"See you soon," shouted the twins, throwing kisses.

They watched the car roll away.

"Next time we see the car, we'll be going home," said Michael.

"Not for two weeks yet," laughed Marsha.

WHAT DO YOU THINK?

1. The Talmud tells us that one of the best forms of ts'doko is that which is offered in secret, so that the one who receives the help is not embarrassed. The Talmud calls this kind of ts'doko *Matan B'sesser*.

   Just before the auction Aaron received an envelope containing twenty-five dollars. The donor did not identify himself. The only thing written on the envelope was, "For Shelanu."

   Who at Kee Tov might have sent it? Give the reason for your answer.

   There are several children whose parents do not pay for their camping at Kee Tov. Their parents can't afford it. The money for their scholarships comes out of a fund created by several men who are interested in helping children who can't afford to attend camp. No one at Kee Tov knows who these children are except Aaron. (Nearly every synagogue has children in its school that attend without paying.)

   Is this Matan B'sesser? Why is this a good way to help the needy?

   Why is it important to help these children go to camp?

2. Another story in the Talmud shows the importance some rabbis attached to Matan B'sesser. A rabbi and his wife left a sum of money each day at the door of a needy neighbor. They always managed to leave the

money before the sun rose so that the neighbor would not know who was giving them the help they needed. The neighbor was very grateful and wanted to know who was being kind to him. One day he and his wife decided to stay awake to find out who was doing it.

In the nick of time the rabbi and his wife discovered that the neighbor was watching for them. They dropped the money quickly and ran away with the neighbor following them at a distance. Rather than risk discovery, the rabbi and his wife hid in a hot oven.

Is this Matan B'sesser? Why?

3. Jeff's brother is studying at the Massachusetts Institute of Technology on a scholarship. Because he is a worthy student, an organization of M.I.T. graduates is lending him the money for his education. When Jeff's brother graduates and gets a position, he will repay the money and perhaps add some more so that the organization can keep helping other deserving students.

The Talmud says, "The highest form of ts'doko is a loan or a gift. Greater is he that lends than he that gives. Greater still is he that lends, and with that loan, helps the needy to help himself."

Why do you think the Talmud teaches this kind of ts'doko?

How is the M.I.T. organization helping to carry out this Talmudic teaching?

What will Jeff's brother have to do to show his gratitude for the help he is receiving?

Appoint children in the class to find out about the various organizations in your community who help the needy. After you hear the reports, see if you can tell how these organizations obey God's mitzvah in the Bible that commands us to:

WITHHOLD NOT GOOD FROM HIM TO WHOM IT IS DUE

WHEN IT IS IN THE POWER OF THY HAND TO DO IT.

Are our organizations today carrying out the ancient laws of the Bible that concern helping the needy?

How? How have we changed the laws today to fit into our modern way of living?

As a special project make posters that show what these organizations are doing for their neighbors who need help. Find out if the Keren Ami money you collect in your religious school is sent to any of these organizations.

Why is it important for you to remember your Keren Ami every week?

4. In the Bible we read, "God dressed Himself with ts'doko like a coat of armor." Gramps explained to the children that a coat of armor is made of many links. No matter how small, each link adds to the strength of the coat. Every bit that we give to a worthy cause counts, no matter how little it is.

What did Gramps say to Tamar that means the same thing? How were the campers at Kee Tov working with God as partners in their Tombola project?

Tell how the following at Kee Tov did his or her share in the Tombola project:
   Emes? S'goolo? Marsha? Her grandparents? Matt? Gramps? Aaron? Joe? Bill? Esther? Mr. McDonald? Laurie's grandmother? The parents?

How do the people of the State of Israel work with God as partners in doing their ts'doko?

Have you ever had the same kind of problem Jeff had, where it was hard to give something away, even though you knew you should? What did you do? Did anyone help you with the problem? Who?

Do you think Jeff was giving real ts'doko with his heart? Why? Why not?

Do you think that as long as Jeff finally gave his birdhouse away, his spirit of giving was all right? Why? Why not?

Is it better to help grudgingly than not to help at all? Why?

Do you like Michael's suggestion to Jeff persuading

him to cooperate with the other boys? What would you have done if you had been there?

5. Last spring, the home of the Ross gardner, Mike, burned down. Mike, his wife, and their four children were left homeless, without clothes or furniture. When the Ross family heard about the misfortune they decided to do something about it. Mr. Ross called the owners of several apartment houses, and was able to locate an apartment. Mrs. Ross called many of her friends and persuaded them to search in their homes for any furniture they could spare. She also asked them for clothing for the children. The twins canvassed the neighborhood for toys and kitchenware. The Ross family was able to interest many people and it wasn't very long before Mike and his family were comfortable again.

How did the Rosses obey God's commandment in the Bible, "If there be among you a needy man, you shall surely open your hand and lend him enough for his needs"?

Have you ever had an experience when you ran a project with a group of friends to help the needy? Tell us about it.

Does this prove that even children who have little money can still help someone who needs help? How? Pretend that you are members of the Ross family.

You hear about Mike's misfortune. Act out the scene. What did Mother say? Daddy? Michael? Marsha? Pretend that each one telephoned a friend.

Act out the telephone conversations. The play can have two acts. Act One can be called "Hearing the News." Act Two can be called, "Ts'doko in Action!"

6. Bill told this story from the Midrash to the boys the night of the Tombola:

   There was once a rich farmer who lost his fortune. So poor did he become that he was forced to work long hours in a field belonging to a neighbor. One day as he was plowing, Elijah appeared dressed as an Arab.

   "You are going to enjoy seven years of your life in

plenty," said Elijah. "There is one decision you must make, however. You will have to decide when you want these seven good years—now, or when you are old."

The astonished farmer thought about the wonderful offer. Finally, he turned to Elijah and said, "You are very kind, but it is my habit to discuss everything that happens with my wife. I cannot give you an answer until I talk with her."

Elijah agreed. When he returned for his answer, the farmer said, "My wife has advised me to take the seven good years now. Is that satisfactory to you?"

Elijah kept his promise. A short while later the farmer found a rich treasure as he was plowing in the ground. He became wealthy once more. Again the wife advised her husband, "Now that we are in a position to help the needy, let us do all in our power. Perhaps then God will help us to have more than seven good years."

For seven years the farmer and his wife searched out every chance to do good deeds. Each day that passed saw them help someone in need. No one was left unaided. When the seven years were up, Elijah returned to take back his gift. Again the farmer refused to take any action until he had talked with his wife. This time the wife returned with her husband and said to Elijah, "We will gladly and willingly return the wonderful gift which your kindness has given to us if you can find another couple who have given to the poor as we have given."

Elijah thought about her wise answer and was convinced that these good people had used their riches wisely. "Keep the gift," he said. "You have surely earned it."

Why do you think Bill told the boys the story?

How is this story from the Midrash like the Bible quotation, "Cast thy bread upon the waters, for thou shalt find it after many days"?

Does this mean that when you help the poor you will get a reward?

How does this tie in with, "Love your neighbor as yourself"?

The boys clamored for another story and Bill told them this one from the Chasidic Rabbis.

A rabbi was known for his kindness to everyone. He could not bear to see anyone in need and helped in whatever way he could. One day a hungry beggar came to his door seeking bread. The rabbi's wife couldn't slice the bread because it was freshly baked and she was afraid it would dry out if she cut it. But the rabbi insisted that she give the bread to the beggar.

Sometime later the rabbi was traveling through a mountainous country. On the road he was captured by a gang of thieves, robbed of his belongings, and brought before their chief. The chief recognized the rabbi as the one who had given him the bread when he was a beggar. He released the rabbi, returning all his possessions.

What quotation from the Bible is like this story?

Do you think the rabbi helped the beggar because he expected a reward? What reward did the rabbi really get?

Do you think Jeff felt better after he gave the bird-house to Shelanu, even though he didn't want to give it away at first? Why?

Could the quotation, "Cast thy bread upon the waters . . ." also mean that the true reward is really the feeling of happiness you get when you help someone more unfortunate than you? Why?

7. When Ben's brother was Bar Mitzvah, Ben's parents asked friends and relatives not to give gifts to their son, but instead to use the gift money for a worthy charity of their choice, in honor of the Bar Mitzvah. They believed that it is the Jewish way of life to give ts'doko when a happy event occurs in the life of the family.

How do Ben's parents thank God for His loving-kindness?

Would you like your parents to do as Ben's parents did? Why? Why not?

15. THE MUSIC BOX

Sara opened the package from Switzerland and drew out a red music box. The china top was decorated with dainty white flowers. Buzzing with excitement, the girls clustered around Sara watching her wind the key. They listened to the tinkling tune.

"It's Brahms' Lullaby!" cried Sara, happily. "Mother and Daddy bought it for me because they know it's my favorite song."

Ann's eyes shone the brightest. She had fallen in love with the music box the moment she had seen it. "Please let me hold it," she begged Sara. "It's the loveliest box I've ever seen."

With a pleased laugh, Sara handed it to Ann. Turning it around carefully in her hand, Ann gazed at the lovely box. How she wished she had one like it! Lucky Sara to own such a beautiful treasure, she thought, returning the music box.

Sara placed the gift on the table near her bed. Every time the music grew faint she let the girls take turns winding it. No one had eyes or ears for anything else that morning.

Miriam had to speak three times before the girls heard her.

"I don't think the music box will be safe here in the bunk. With all the hustle and bustle, someone might just accidentally knock it over." She turned to Sara. "Better let me put it in a safe place until you go home."

Sara spoke up quickly, "Please let us keep it here, Miriam. We'll be careful. How can we all enjoy it if you put it away?"

Miriam looked at all the pleading faces. "All right, then, but be careful. One careless movement will shatter that delicate china to pieces." Sara's willingness to share her treasure made Miriam consent, although it was very much against her better judgment.

"Let's keep it there," said Sara, pointing to a shelf above Ann's bed. "That way it'll be out of reach when we don't use it."

Sara's suggestion delighted Ann. She hugged Sara with a happy squeal. "I'll guard it with my very life, Sara," she promised.

"Volley ball game, girls," announced Miriam. Each girl took a last lingering look at the box. Ann hated to leave. How she wished her parents would buy her one! She made up her mind to write and ask them.

Before they left for the volley ball game, Sara asked Miriam if she could show the box to the Y'lodim in the other cabins. Soon all the Y'lodim were gathered around Sara. They listened to the melody twice around.

In the middle of the game Ann hurt her finger as she was hitting the ball over the net. The finger began to swell rapidly. Miriam sent her to the infirmary so Mary could look at it.

Mary examined the finger. "It isn't broken," she said, "but the doctor will be here soon. Let's ask him to look at it just to be sure." Mary bandaged the finger and added, "Stay here until he comes."

Mary handed Ann some books and went on with her work. The thought of the music box came back to Ann. She had to hear the music again. Besides, she'd much rather read a book

she had in her cabin. "I'll be right back," she called to Mary, running out of the infirmary with full speed. "I want to get my own book."

In the cabin she paused to gaze at the music box on the shelf. Sara won't mind if I play it just once, she told herself. She said she wanted to share it with us. Lifting the box from its perch she wound the key and held the box close to her ear. Her eyes closed happily.

A breathing sound made her look up. Susan was standing before her, hands on hips, frowning at the music box in Ann's hand.

"What are you doing here?" Susan demanded.

Ann was embarrassed. "I was—I was—I was—Would you mind repeating that question?"

"You heard me the first time. You're not supposed to be handling that music box. You know how careful we have to be. And besides, you're supposed to be in the infirmary."

Susan's scolding brought a flush to Ann's cheeks. "I suppose you're going to snitch on me now." With a toss of her head Ann put back the music box and picked up her book.

"Maybe I will and maybe I won't," teased Susan.

Ann felt her cheeks growing hot. "Why don't you mind your own business, you old busybody!" she flared. "Go on! Tattle! See if I care!"

Susan's face darkened. "I'm going to tell Miriam just what you said!"

Before Ann could stop herself, she gave Susan a hard slap on the cheek, her hand leaving a streak of red.

"I'll get even with you!" screamed Susan. "You just wait and see!" Shaking her fists, she stalked out of the cabin. Ann could hear a sob in Susan's voice as the door slammed.

Walking slowly back to the infirmary, Ann felt sorry for what she had done. "Why did I have to lose my temper and slap her? She'll never forgive me," she muttered to herself over and over again.

A short time, later, Janet, one of the Y'lodim girls, entered the S'goolo cabin. Her eyes found the music box. Glancing carefully around, she removed it and took it with her to the washroom, closing the door behind her. Janet played the lullaby twice through before she decided to put it back. Just as she passed Ann's trunk she heard a noise on the porch. There was no time to put the box back. Frightened, Janet dropped it into Ann's open trunk, burying it underneath the clothes. Out through the door she hurried. She breathed a sigh of relief when she saw that it was only Lovon. "I'm glad dogs can't talk," she mumbled to herself. "Now no one can tell on me."

After the game the girls returned to their cabin. "My music box! My music box!" Sara cried in alarm. "It's gone!"

They looked everywhere.

Sara sat wailing on her bed, tears streaming down her cheeks. "My lovely gift. What will Mother and Daddy say?" She sobbed as if her heart would break.

The girls were silent. Sara's misery tugged at their hearts. Touching her cheek, Susan thought of the slap Ann had given her. She could still feel the sting. She hadn't told the girls how Ann had behaved. This was a good time to fix Ann.

Turning to Miriam, she said, "Miriam, do you remember when you sent me to the cabin for your whistle? Well, I found Ann here playing the music box. She was the last one to handle it."

Miriam sent Tamar for Ann. When they returned, Ann waved a bandaged finger at them, grinning. "The doctor said I'll live."

Only silence greeted her. Something was wrong! Ann's grin faded at the sight of the disapproving faces. She knew immediately something was wrong. Susan had tattled! Ann lowered her eyes to the floor.

"Ann, Sara's music box is missing," said Miriam in a low voice, "Susan says she saw you playing it while we were on the volley ball field."

Ann's eyes skipped from Miriam to the shelf. Her eyes widened. "I put it back—right there!" She pointed to the spot on the shelf where she had last seen it.

"You must have taken it down again," shouted Susan. "If you put it back, it would still be there!"

"I did put it back! I did! I did! You saw me!" Ann ran over to Sara. "Do you think I'd take anything that wasn't mine? I know I shouldn't have played it and I'm sorry. But I didn't take it!" Ann looked pleadingly at the accusing faces around her. She felt a frantic sense of helplessness.

"I bet you took it and hid it," said Susan. Before anyone could stop her, Susan leaned over Ann's trunk, scattering the clothes in all directions. With a triumphant cry she held up the music box and waved it in the air. "You're a crook!" Susan shouted.

Miriam grabbed the box away from Susan. "We don't use that kind of language at Kee Tov," she said to Susan, "you're not the judge! Stay on the porch until you can control your tongue! I'll speak to you later!"

Susan glared at Ann and stamped out of the cabin.

Tears flooded Ann's eyes. "I didn't put it there! Honest, Miriam! I don't know how it landed in my trunk!" She threw herself on her bed, crying bitterly.

Miriam looked at the silent girls.

Sara was the first to speak. She sat on Ann's bed. "It's all right, Ann," she comforted, "as long as we found it. Let's forget it. Please stop crying."

"But I didn't take it! I'm telling you the truth!" Ann looked at the accusing faces and she shivered. They thought she was a thief! She broke out into fresh tears. Miriam said unhappily, "Sara, do you mind if I put the music box in the office safe until you go home?"

Sara looked at Ann's quivering shoulders. "No, it's caused too much trouble already."

Marsha came over to Ann, seeking to comfort her but the

right words wouldn't come. Instead, she turned away. Was Ann telling the truth? On the other hand, who could possibly be mean enough to hide the music box in Ann's trunk?

Tamar was shocked. How could Ann do such a horrible thing —stealing from her own friend!

Miriam left the cabin. She found Susan sitting on the steps staring into space.

"Are you proud of the way you hurt Ann?" Miriam asked.

"If I did what she did, you'd be plenty cross at me," said Susan, not the least bit sorry. "I didn't tell you this before—but Ann slapped me right across the face when I told her she had no right to handle the box. Was she right?" Susan snapped at Miriam.

"No—it wasn't right, Susan. But you can't be the judge and decide what to do. Especially now, when you're so angry at Ann. You can't judge fairly when you bear a grudge."

Susan bit her lips. Miriam continued. "I've never known Ann to tell a lie. How will you feel if we discover that Ann *didn't* take the box?"

"She's guilty and I proved it!" Susan was sure she was right. Maybe Ann could fool Miriam with her crocodile tears, but she couldn't fool Susan, not for a minute!

The bugle sounded through Kee Tov. With a tired sigh, Miriam gathered the girls for lunch. In the mess hall Ann refused to eat. A dark feeling of loneliness swept over her. Her friends were deserting her one by one for something she hadn't done. Miriam took her aside. "Look, Ann," she said, "I know that things look bad. But if you're telling the truth, then you know it deep down in your heart. No one can take that away from you. But you can't run away from what has happened. Face up to it! If you face the girls with truth in your heart, the truth will reach out to them and make them believe you." Miriam hoped that Ann would understand and be comforted. The more she thought about Ann's grief, the more she believed Ann *was* telling the truth. She decided to ask Dorothy to gather the Y'lodim girls together and talk to them. Perhaps one of them could help clear up the mystery.

During lunch, Susan gave a note to Marsha. She handed one to Tamar and one to Sara. "Meet me in the Thinking Place for an important discussion," said the note. When the four girls met, Susan began immediately to talk. "Our bunk has been disgraced. As bunk delegate, I feel responsible. We have to do something about it. Ann stole the music box and we have to make her admit it. She can't get away with her crime."

Marsha spoke up quickly, "Wait a minute, Susan. We're not sure Ann did it. What if she's telling the truth?"

"Don't be such a softie, Marsha," scoffed Susan, waving away Marsha's words. "We proved it when I pulled the box out of her trunk." Susan's next words made Marsha gasp. "Let's not talk to Ann until she confesses her wicked deed. All those in favor, raise your right hand."

Pale but determined, Marsha interrupted the vote. "That's not fair. You're being mean, Susan, and you know it. A person isn't guilty until you've proved it beyond a doubt!" Marsha's voice rose with excitement.

But Susan hardly listened. "All those in favor, raise your right hand," she repeated, looking daggers at Marsha.

Marsha refused to be ignored. She swallowed before she spoke again. "I'm not going to vote—and that's final. If I were in Ann's place, I wouldn't want her to vote against me without proof." She turned a pleading glance to Tamar and Sara. "Would you?" she asked, looking them straight in the eyes.

"But Marsha," said Tamar, "Susan's right. We can't let Ann get away with stealing. She should admit it." Tamar couldn't understand Marsha's defense of Ann when the honor of the bunk was at stake.

"Ann's afraid to admit it now," said Sara, suddenly angry at Ann for depriving the whole bunk of the pleasure of the music box.

Marsha realized she was appealing to deaf ears. "Count me

out!" she said, with disgust. The vote was three to one. "Every time Ann speaks to us we'll freeze her," said Susan. Sara and Tamar nodded their agreement.

Marsha ran out of the Thinking Place.

She was very disturbed. How could Susan be so cruel? How could the girls be willing to agree with such an unfair plan? What was she going to do? She couldn't ask Gramps for help! Nor could she ask Miriam. She'd be tattling on her own friends. Still, she couldn't let them make Ann suffer. She thought of her parents. If only they were at Kee Tov at that very moment. They'd know what to do. But that was useless, too—they weren't there. She had to decide for herself. Should she ask Michael? No—then Bill might find out. "What would God want me to do?" she asked herself out loud. As soon as she asked herself that question, she knew. God would want her to help Ann. Right now Ann needed a friend more than anything else in the world. She decided to tell Ann about the freeze and then, no matter what, to stick close to her side wherever she went. Together they'd solve the problem.

As soon as Marsha made the decision, she felt as if a heavy weight had been lifted from her shoulders. She ran to find Ann. After searching, she finally found her sitting on a stone behind the cabin, looking like a lost ghost.

Marsha came right to the point. "Ann, did you hide the music box?"

"No!" Ann's freckled face looked squarely at Marsha.

"Is that the honest truth?"

"Yes!"

"I believe you," said Marsha. And she did! Beyond any doubt she knew that Ann was telling the truth. "How can we prove it to the girls?"

"I don't know." The hopeless feeling inside Ann nearly choked her. "Unless," she said slowly, "we can get the one who did do it to confess."

"The girls are planning to freeze you, Ann. I'm telling you so you'll be prepared. I told them to count me out." Marsha's thoughts raced ahead of her tongue. "I don't know why Susan is being so mean. It isn't like her at all."

"She's mad at me because I slapped her and told her to mind her own business. She's trying to get even with me. I know I was wrong and I was going to apologize. But everything happened so fast I didn't get the chance."

Marsha thought for a minute. "Would you apologize now?"

"I'll do anything. It's awful to lose all your friends at once—that is, all except you." Ann gave Marsha a shadow of a smile.

"Maybe if you say you're sorry, Susan won't go through with the freeze," said Marsha, hopefully. "Tamar and Sara will do what Susan does."

They left to find Susan. But Ann had to postpone the apology. Dorothy sent for all the Y'lodim girls.

"Girls," she said, "something happened in S'goolo this morning and one of our girls is being blamed for something she didn't do." Dorothy went on to tell them about the disappearance of the music box and its recovery in Ann's trunk. "I know that the girl who is getting the blame is telling the truth." Dorothy sought out Ann and looked squarely at her.

"See!" whispered Marsha to Ann with a smile, "Dorothy believes you, too. And Miriam does. The others will, too. Wait and see!"

Dorothy continued, "If anyone knows anything, please tell us. I'm sure that no one here at Kee Tov would want someone to take the blame for her mistake. Please help us to clear up the mystery. If you've made a mistake, get it off your chest. You'll feel better."

Janet listened. A voice inside her urged her to tell Dorothy, but she was afraid. She didn't have the courage to admit what she had done.

The girls were true to their promise. They ignored Ann completely. When they saw how close Marsha stuck to Ann's side, they gave Marsha the frozen treatment, too.

"Tell Susan now how sorry you are," whispered Marsha to Ann. "Maybe it will help."

"I can't, Marsha." Dark doubts gripped Ann like an octopus. "She won't listen. She's too angry."

Marsha knew Ann was right. It was too late!

No one was happy in S'goolo that night. The air was filled with suspicion and unhappiness. Miriam was at a loss. The problem was beyond her. She decided to discuss the problem with Aaron in the morning. Everyone prepared for bed. Never had the cabin been so quiet.

That night, Janet added an extra sentence to her prayers. "Please, God," she prayed, "forgive me for not telling Dorothy I hid the music box. I know I was wrong but I was too ashamed." For a long time she couldn't fall asleep.

Later that night, Janet had a dream. She found herself in the Thinking Place. All at once, her back felt heavy. When she looked over her shoulder she saw a rocket strapped to her back. Gramps appeared, wheeling a barrel. He attached a hose made of macaroni to the top of her rocket and pumped a handle on the barrel. A fountain of white foam gushed out of the top of the rocket, splashing over Janet's face. She looked as if she were taking a shave. Janet tasted the foam and discovered that it was root beer. "Think of that!" she said to herself. "My rocket is being fueled with root beer!"

"Prepare for blast off!" shouted Gramps to her. "10—8—6—4 —zero hour! Say hello to a star for me, Janet!" Gramps gave her a mighty shove and with a thundering roar, Janet soared through the night. Zooming ahead she zigged and she zagged. She became a castaway in space.

In her path stood the Big Bear. She flew toward its starry dipper to shout a friendly hello. "Stay away from me, Janet!" growled the Big Bear, flashing its golden lights. "I want nothing to do with you. You didn't confess that you hid the music box."

With a frightened cry, Janet swerved away and flew onward.

The Dog Star dropped on her hair, but when it recognized her, it shook itself off with a fiery shiver. "I'm particular where I rest," it barked, wagging its blazing tail.

Before her spread the Milky Way. It shot a stream of milk at Janet, making her cry jumbo white tears. She nose-dived into a loop.

"Can't you see I'm sorry," shouted Janet. But the stars flipped their twinkles at her and blazed back. "Prove it! Tell them about the music box!"

A comet with a flaming tail streaked by Janet. As it flew past, it peppered her with hot sparks. She felt as if she were inside a volcano. Spinning in another direction she smacked square into the moon. "Ouch!" yelled Janet, holding her burned nose.

On the moon she bounced about like a rubber ball.

A tall green building guarded the entrance to the moon. On it was a sign that said, "Kee Tov Cheese Factory." Janet pushed open the door and found herself in a room as tall as a sky-scraper. Rolls of green cheeses with great black tunnels running through them stood on spindly legs. Janet leaped up and streaked through one of the tunnels. A cheese blocked her when she slid out. Pointing a cheesy finger at her, it said in a cheesy voice, "Out you go! You let someone take the blame for something *you* did!" Sadly, Janet ran out of the cheese factory.

Now she bounced up into the air and landed flat on her face on top of a towering mountain. To her surprise the mountain was made of chocolate bars with "Kee Tov" printed on each one. But when Janet tried to eat a bar, the chocolate turned to sawdust. She spit it out with distaste and heard the mountain rumble with chocolate laughter. Off the moon she tumbled. "You'd better do something about that music box before it's too late!" thundered the mountain after her.

Next she met Draco, the Dragon. Blocking her path with a curtain of fire he blinked his stars off and on like an unfriendly spotlight. Draco rolled out a long scroll of star paper. In a dragon roar he began to read, dotting each sentence with a flaming hot period. Everything he read was about Janet. It told about every wrong thing she had done that day at Kee Tov.

When he finished, Draco bombarded Janet with star gas, loosening her rocket. Down she spiraled. Over Kee Tov she hovered for a while and then she became a Janet-copter drifting down to earth.

The soft thud awoke her and she sat up screaming. "I did it! I did it! I hid the music box!"

Everyone in the cabin awoke with a start.

Ruth, Janet's counselor, came running. Janet looked at Ruth as if she didn't know her. She heard Ruth tell the other girls to go back to bed.

"You go back to sleep, too, Janet," she said, trying to calm the trembling girl. "You've had a nightmare!"

Janet shook her head, "I'm afraid." And then Janet told Ruth about the dream and how she hid the music box. She ended with, "I didn't mean to take it! Honest, I didn't. I just wanted to hear the pretty music again. I've been feeling terrible since Dorothy asked us about it."

Ruth understood immediately. She tried to comfort Janet. "As long as you've admitted it, Janet, everything will be all right. Go back to sleep. We'll talk about it in the morning."

When Janet fell asleep again, Ruth dressed and hurried to tell Miriam about Janet's confession. After Ruth left, Miriam didn't hesitate for a second. On went the lights! She told the girls what had happened without mentioning Janet's name.

For the first time that day, Ann felt happy. Turning to Marsha, she gave her an extra special smile.

"I told you everything would be all right," said Marsha, smiling back. She bounced out of bed to hug Ann.

Susan, Tamar, and Sara said nothing. A feeling of shame crept slowly over them.

"Susan," said Ann, breaking the silence, "I've been wanting to tell you how sorry I am. I shouldn't have slapped you." Ann's voice pleaded with Susan to forgive her.

Susan found the right words at last. "I'm the one who should ask forgiveness. I don't know what got into me."

The Spirit of Forgiveness flew through the cabin. Joy filled Ann's heart nearly to bursting. She had friends again.

Miriam switched off the lights. "It says in the Bible," she quoted, smiling in the darkness, " 'In justice shall you judge your fellow man.' "

"I know I wasn't fair, Miriam," said Susan. "I guess I'd better say that to myself five times a day."

"It's something we all have to say, Susan," replied Miriam. Then after a pause, she spoke again. "Marsha, you remind me of somebody."

"Me?" asked Marsha.

"Yes, you," laughed Miriam. "She lived in the days of the Bible and her name was Deborah. She was a wise judge in Israel and people came to her from far and near when they had quarrels to settle. It was because of her courage that Barak finally went to battle and defeated the enemy at Mt. Tabor. The courage you showed in sticking to Ann was like Deborah's courage. And the justice you showed was like the justice Deborah showed under the palm tree where she held court."

Marsha was glad it was dark in the cabin. She felt a blush creep over her face. "Imagine that!" she murmured drowsily to herself. "Miriam thinks I'm like Deborah in the Bible! If only I could be like her!"

WHAT DO YOU THINK?

1. Isaiah, the prophet, spoke out again and again against injustice. He said that a person should not judge by what he sees, nor give a decision because of what people say.

   The prophet, Amos, spoke out against injustice with these words:

But let justice well up as waters,
And righteousness as a mighty stream.

The prophet, Micah, spoke out against injustice, too. He said:

It hath been told thee, O man, what is good,
And what the Lord doth require of thee:
Only to do justly, and to love mercy, and to walk
  humbly with thy God.

The prophets were courageous men who taught that God wanted His people to live just and righteous lives—to seek truth and love and mercy. Their words are as true today as they were in the days of the Bible.
Notice what Micah put first.

How did Susan disobey the words of the prophets in the way she treated Ann?

Pretend that the prophets came to Kee Tov on a visit the next day.
  Dramatize what you think Amos, Isaiah, and Micah would say to Susan. To Marsha. To Tamar. To Sara. To Ann. To Miriam. To Janet.
  Try to include the good deeds of the girls in S'goolo as well as their mistakes. Don't forget to mention Sara's willingness to share her music box and Susan's apology for her bad behavior.

Can you think of a time when you or someone you know was treated unfairly and accused of something you didn't do? What happened? Did someone help you? Who?

Did Ann's behavior make her seem innocent? Why? Why not?

2. In the Midrash we read that Joseph had his silver cup hidden in the sack of his brother Benjamin before the brothers left Egypt to return to Jacob, their father. As the brothers were on their way, Joseph sent his servants to find the cup. When the servants drew the cup from Benjamin's sack, his brothers in their rage shouted at him, "You thief! Now you have brought shame upon us!" They hit him and spoke harshly to him all the way back to

Joseph's palace. Benjamin bore the blows and rough language in patient silence even though he knew that he hadn't taken the cup. By telling this story, the rabbis tried to show people how they ought to behave when they are unjustly accused.

How did Susan behave like Joseph's brothers?

What did Marsha say in the story that Joseph's brothers should have known?

What did Miriam say in the story that Joseph's brothers should have known?

3. Marsha received the Torah of justice for S'goolo the following Friday night. When Aaron presented the Torah he said, "In the Talmud we are told, 'The world is run by two spinning wheels—one that spins justice and one that spins mercy.'" He also quoted these words from the Talmud, "There can be no justice unless mercy is a part of it."

To whom in S'goolo did these words apply? Why?

List all the ways in which Marsha mixed justice with mercy.

How did Susan fail to measure up to justice mixed with mercy?

4. In the Talmud we read, "He who knows testimony on behalf of his fellow man and does not give that testimony is one whom God dislikes."

How did Janet disobey this Talmud rule?

Why did God dislike what Janet did?

Have you ever been in a position to help prove someone's innocence? What did you do? Did it take special courage? Why?

How did you feel when you were able to help prove your friend's innocence?

5. The Ninth Commandment says, "Bear not false witness against your fellow man."

How is this like the Talmud rule above?

*Could a false witness be someone who doesn't take
the blame for something he did and allows another
to take his blame instead? How?*

*Can you think of a time when you were blamed for
something you didn't do and no one came forward
to prove you innocent? What did you do?*

How is this like Emes B'libo?

Does a false witness have truth in his heart?

*What did Miriam tell Ann about Emes B'libo? Do
you agree with her? Why? Why not?*

6. Another Talmud story tells us about the rabbi who
stayed at the home of a friend. The friend treated
the rabbi with great respect and honor. He tried to
make the rabbi feel at home and did all he could to
make him comfortable and happy. Several years
later, the rabbi was in the courtroom judging a case.
He looked up to see the friend standing before him.

They greeted each other warmly. "Why are you
in my court?" asked the rabbi.

"I have come before you to try a case. I am glad
you are the judge. Do you remember how well I
treated you when you were a guest in my home?"

"Yes," replied the rabbi, "I remember it well.
However, I shall have to give your case to another
judge. I cannot try your case now."

"Why not?" asked the friend, in surprise.

"Because you have reminded me of other favors,"
said the rabbi, and he refused to judge the case.

*How does this tie in with the Talmud rule, "A judge
should not stand in judgment over a person he likes
or dislikes"?*

*Did Susan's dislike of Ann at the time she acted like
a judge have anything to do with her actions? Do
you think she was getting back at Ann for the slap
or do you feel she really believed she was right?*

*Can you remember a time when someone wanted
you to pay him back for a favor he had done for you?
Did you think he was fair to hold you to that kind
of bargain?*

7. The Jews always believed that all men are equal. The story of Naboth and his vineyard in the Bible proves that even a king could be unjust and be punished for his evil deeds.

Naboth had a wonderful vineyard near the palace of King Ahab in Samaria. Ahab looked at the rich grapes and wanted the vineyard for himself. He came to Naboth. "Give me your vineyard," he said, "and I will exchange it for a finer field. I want it because it is so near the palace."

"No," said Naboth firmly, "it has belonged to my family for many generations and I want my sons to have it, too."

Ahab went sadly back to the palace and told his queen, Jezebel, about Naboth and his refusal to give him the land.

"Think nothing more about it, Ahab, my husband. I will get the vineyard for you. No one dares to refuse a king what he wants."

Jezebel sent two of her trusted servants to Naboth's village with letters she forged in Naboth's name. The servants went before the judges and said, "We heard Naboth curse God." Naboth said he didn't say anything like that, but the men ignored him and asked, "What shall we do to the man who talks like this about God?"

"Let him be killed!" shouted the people in one voice.

And so Naboth was put to death and his vineyard became the king's.

Elijah heard of the cruel deed and came fearlessly to Ahab. "God will punish you and your family," he warned. "Not even a king can do what you have done and go free."

Later, Ahab repented of his sin. But he was killed at the battle-front and his kingdom was overthrown.

How was Marsha like Elijah?

How did Ahab disobey the Tenth Commandment that says, "You shall not keep thinking and wanting what your neighbor has"? How does this tie in with so-me-ach b'chelko?

Were Naboth's people fair to kill him without a trial?

8. In the Book of Proverbs in the Bible we find the following words:

"Go to the ant, thou sluggard; Consider her ways and be wise. Having no chief or ruler she provides her bread in the summer and gathers her harvest."

A Rabbi in the Talmud wanted to discover for himself whether this was true. Knowing that ants dislike the sun, he went out into a field and spread his coat over an ant hill. A single ant popped out from under the cloak. Wanting to be able to identify it, the Rabbi splashed it with green paint. The green ant scurried back under the coat. Soon it returned bringing with it a company of ants, all seeking shade. But meanwhile, the Rabbi had removed the cloak. He saw the company turn on the green ant who had lured them into the sun, and kill it.

The Rabbi looked sadly at the green ant and said, "If these ants had had a ruler or a leader, they would have set up a judge and given the ant a fair trial."

Was the Rabbi right? Why?

Was the trial Susan gave Ann a fair one? Why? Why not?

Do you think Susan had good reason to behave as she did towards Ann? Remember, Ann had slapped her face and called her a tattle-tale. What would you have done to Ann? Do you think she deserved to be punished for taking the music box without permission?

*Why did Miriam say Marsha was like Deborah in the Bible? Was it because she was **courageous** like Deborah or was it because she was **just** like Deborah— or both?*

Who was the better leader, Susan or Marsha? Why?

What do you think of the way Tamar and Sara acted in the Thinking Place? Were they following the wrong leader? Why?

9. In Susan's classroom Betsy stole a quarter from Nancy's desk. One of the children saw Betsy take the quarter out of her shoe when the children were

going home. She told the teacher, and she also told some of her classmates.

A short time afterwards some more money was missing from the teacher's desk, this time a dime. Immediately, the children and the teacher looked at Betsy. Betsy kept saying that she didn't take the money. But everybody acted as if she were guilty— including the teacher. Later that day, the dime was found behind the teacher's desk.

Write the ending to this story.

What should Susan have learned from this incident?

What quotations from the Bible and Talmud does this story illustrate?

Have you ever had anything like this happen to you? What did you do?

10. Last fall, Michael's rocket ship was taken from the porch where he left it overnight. The next day, while he was playing with his friend, Dickie, he spied the rocket in Dickie's playroom. Michael accused Dickie of stealing his rocket and refused to believe Dickie when he said his father had bought him the rocket at the toy store. Michael ran home very upset and told his mother.

Mrs. Ross was upset, too, because she had picked up the rocket on the porch and hidden it to teach Michael a lesson not to leave his things on the porch.

Write an ending to this story. Choose the best ending and dramatize it.

How is this story like the one in Susan's classroom?

How is this story like The Music Box?

What quotation from the Talmud would you use to illustrate this story?

11. The Torah says, "Do not follow even a majority of the people when they are going to do a great evil."

How did Marsha, Tamar, and Sara act when it became a question of going along with the rest of the bunk?

Have you ever had to stand up alone or with one or two people against a group like Marsha?

Tell the story to your class—but don't finish it. Let your classmates decide what they would have done. Then tell them the truth about what you did.

16. WHO IS THE BRAVEST HERO?

Michael and Jeff stood before a square glass cage in the science museum. They were watching the two praying-mantises Jeff had caught on Universal Lawn.

"See how they hold their legs close to their chests," said Jeff.

"They look like they're saying their prayers," chuckled Michael, bending to get a closer look.

Jeff rapped the bottom of the cage playfully. Both boys laughed when the praying-mantises began to box each other. Spearing a small piece of hamburger with a toothpick, Jeff held it over the mouths of the insects. They grabbed at the food. Next, Jeff held out a teaspoonful of water. The insects sipped the water, daintily. To the boys' delight, they washed their grandfather faces in the remaining water.

"How can they possibly wash their faces in so little water?" asked Michael.

"If a praying-mantis is really hungry," explained Jeff, "he'll eat his own leg, or even the leg of his relatives. I once read about a scientist who painted a wasp green and dipped it in shellac. He fed the mess to some praying-mantises and they ate it without even blinking an eye!"

"You'd think they'd get a stomachache with that combination, wouldn't you?" Michael looked admiringly at Jeff. Boy! Jeff certainly knew his science!

At that moment they heard a fierce barking outside the museum. Before they could investigate, Lovon came bounding in through the open door. Following close on his heels came Paul, one of the Y'lodim, waving a big stick.

"Come back here, you dumb dog!" shouted Paul. "When I get through with you, you'll never jump at me again!"

Thoroughly frightened, Lovon ran for protection. He wedged himself between Michael and Jeff. They whipped around to face Paul. The stick in Paul's hand, the flush on his cheeks, and the terror in Lovon's eyes showed Michael all that was wrong. He leaped at Paul, trying to grab his stick. They tangled like a pair of fierce bulls. The next thing Michael knew, he was sitting on Paul's stomach, pinning him down to the floor.

"Get the stick, Jeff," Michael yelled, "while I hold him!"

Jeff had to force Paul's fingers open before he could pry the stick loose.

Paul squirmed. "You don't even know why I had to hit that stupid dog," he cried, twisting his body back and forth. "How would you like it if he broke the ash tray you had made for your mother's birthday? I'm going to fix him! He always jumps on me when he sees me. He made me break the ash tray when I was carrying it to the oven to be baked!"

The scowl on Michael's face darkened. "That's no excuse for hitting a defenseless animal. He's an animal and doesn't know any better!"

"That's what you think! I'm going to hit him again and again until he learns his lesson!"

Jeff dragged Lovon over to Michael to show him a red streak glowing through Lovon's white fur. Michael's anger boiled over like coffee in a pot. Glaring down at Paul he shouted, "If you don't promise to leave Lovon alone, I'm going to bash your face in! And if you think I'm fooling, just try hitting that dog again!"

The fury in Michael's eyes told Paul that Michael meant exactly what he had said. "I promise," he said, sullenly.

Michael released Paul and he backed out of the museum, muttering to himself. When he reached the door, he clenched his fists at them. "You'll be sorry. Don't think you won't!" With a swift kick at the door, Paul left.

The boys examined Lovon's back carefully. Luckily, there was no break in the skin.

Kneeling on one knee, Michael took Lovon's face in his hands and rubbed his face in the dog's soft fur. Lovon's tail began to wag slowly and he lapped Michael's cheek with a grateful tongue.

"Do you think we ought to tell Bill?" asked Jeff, worried at Paul's threat.

"We'd better not," answered Michael, shaking his head. "If we tell, Paul might take it out on Lovon. Anyway he promised he wouldn't hurt Lovon any more." Michael wanted to believe Paul with all his heart. But he couldn't seem to shake the uneasy feeling that was beginning to grow. Would Paul keep his promise? What if he tried to get even with Michael and Jeff?

Michael had good reason to feel the way he did!

Without losing any time, Paul gathered his bunkmates together. "Michael and Jeff attacked me in the science museum," he announced. "Jeff twisted my arm and Michael pummeled me in the stomach." Paul clutched his stomach and doubled up with imitation pain.

His bunkmates were all eyes and ears. It was hard to believe that Michael and Jeff would hurt anyone that way. They stared at him in silence. "What started the fight?" asked Saul.

"Lovon jumped on me and made me break the ash tray I was holding. All I did was slap him on the back—just a light touch—and before I knew it, Michael had me pinned to the floor and Jeff was helping him!"

Paul's listeners grew more and more astonished as Paul told one lie after another. He forgot to clutch his stomach in his excitement. "And that wasn't all," he added, when he came to the end of his story. "Michael said he was the boss of all the Y'lodim at Kee Tov and we'd just better follow his orders —or else!"

"That Michael needs a good lesson," said Seth. "Let's tell Aaron—" Paul interrupted Seth with a quick, "No! Telling Aaron won't do any good. Let's handle Michael and Jeff ourselves."

"What'll we do?" asked Johnnie, jutting his lower lip forward. "Michael can't get away with that kind of trick."

"Let's get them before the campfire and beat them up," suggested Abner, pummeling the air with his fist.

"Aaron won't like that," said Saul, suddenly afraid he'd get into trouble. "Let's tell him what happened. He'll know what to do."

Paul held his stomach again and moaned. "Whose side are you on?" he demanded, glaring at Saul, "mine or Michael's? Are we going to let him get away with saying he's boss of Kee Tov? Aaron doesn't need to know—and that's final!"

The boys nodded in agreement—all except Saul. When Paul saw Saul's hesitation, he again flared at him. "If you're too chicken to help—then don't! Just don't count on us to help you when you're in trouble!"

Saul's ears turned bright red. He wasn't chicken. Paul knew that. "All right," he agreed. "I'll join the gang. Just tell me what to do."

Paul bent closer to the boys, his voice barely a whisper. "Let's spoil their farm skit tonight. Michael's in charge. We'll keep him from being there." Paul thought for a long minute. "You know that tool shed on Universal Lawn near the chapel? Let's lock Michael up in there until after the campfire this evening."

"How'll we get him there?" asked Abner.

"I heard Gramps tell Michael he could use the garden tools in the shed for his skit. When Michael goes to get them, we'll lock him up."

"How'll we get the key to lock him up?" asked Seth.

"I'll get it from the chapel when Gramps isn't looking," said Paul.

"That's a neat trick," said Johnnie, gleefully. "That'll teach him not to buck up against us guys!"

After supper, Michael ran to get the tools for the skit. On the way he met Seth, Paul's bunkmate. "Isn't it a dandy night for our last campfire?" Michael asked Seth, his face shining with excitement.

Suddenly, Seth felt a twinge of conscience. He heard himself say, "Yes," but he couldn't look Michael straight in the eye.

"See you at the campfire tonight," laughed Michael, hurrying away.

Seth followed his racing figure. Doubts began to trouble him. They grew stronger and stronger. Were the boys being too hard on Michael? After all, he hadn't hurt them. Did they really want the campfire to be a flop? And Paul, was he telling the truth about Michael? Paul had been caught telling lies before—especially when he wanted his own way. Seth walked slowly toward his bunk, busy with his thoughts. But it was too late now. Paul was in back of the shed right this minute waiting for Michael. Seth's eyes clouded. He felt as if an axe were about to fall.

At the shed, Michael opened the door. Standing in the corner were the tools he needed. As he leaned over to gather them, he heard the key turn in the lock with a loud click.

Through the door he heard a loud laugh. "I said I'd fix you. Well, I'm doing just that. Let's see you put on your skit at the campfire now!"

Michael gasped. He heard Paul laugh again and then there was silence.

Inside, Michael looked around for a way out. Not a window in the place! He pushed, he thumped, and he kicked, but it was no use. The door wouldn't budge. What was he going to do? No one would dream of looking for him here. His head was spinning. What a low-down trick! He paced the shed like a caged tiger.

Paul took a roundabout way back to his cabin. It might arouse suspicion if anyone saw him coming from Universal Lawn. Down the hill he ran, along the lake front far below the Big House. Two huge logs lay directly in his path. With a running leap he jumped to clear them. But he didn't quite make it! Instead, he landed with his right foot caught between the logs. The logs rolled together, wedging his foot tightly between them. Twisting and turning, Paul tried to pull his leg out. But the more he struggled, the more he walled up his foot. He tried to push the logs apart, but they were too heavy.

His shouts for help filled the air. But only silence greeted him. What a tough break, he thought, just when things were working out his way! He kept twisting his foot, but stopped after a while. What if he broke his ankle? Into his pocket went his hand looking for something that might help him. But all he felt was the key to the shed. Now both Michael and he were trapped! His bunkmates knew where Michael was— but who would think of looking for him here? Nobody came here at this time of the day. What if nobody found him and he had to stay here all night! His fear mounted higher and higher. His foot began to feel like the old tree logs that had caught him in their grip. And then another thought began to torment him. Was he being punished for what he had done to Michael? He drew a frightened breath and wiped the hot tears that began to flow down his cheeks. Again he shouted for help.

Down by the lake Gramps was taking his nightly walk. Suddenly, he heard a shriek bounce off the trees. It was followed by loud cries of, "Help! I'm stuck! Won't someone help me!" Gramps hurried toward the sound.

Gramps quickly sized up the situation the moment he saw Paul. Standing on one log with both feet, Gramps rolled the second one away, freeing Paul's foot. Gramp examined the foot carefully, moving the ankle back and forth gently. Luckily there were no skin breaks, only a red mark where the logs had rubbed against it.

"I guess the foot is all right," said Gramps. "Better let Mary look at it to make sure." Gramps took Paul's arm to help him to the infirmary. But Paul didn't move. He looked towards the shed and he looked into Gramps' kind eyes. Lowering his head, he kicked the earth with his stiff foot. His heart pounded like a drum. For the first time that day he realized how wrong he had been.

And then the whole story spilled out of him. He didn't leave out a single thing.

Gramps had only one thing to say at that minute. "Let's get Michael first." They hurried to the shed.

As Paul opened the door, Michael fell out. Puffing up at Gramps, he cried with relief, "I thought I'd have to be there all night. How did you find me?"

Before Gramps had a chance to answer, Michael saw Paul standing to one side. Michael's lips tightened. He rose slowly with fire in his eyes, clenching his fists. "I'm going to clobber you!" he shouted, leaping at Paul.

Gramps rushed to pull the two boys apart.

"Hold on, Michael," he said firmly, "there's already been enough anger at Kee Tov today. Let's talk a little—that is, when you calm down."

"There's nothing to talk about, Gramps," said Michael through white lips. "He's the meanest skunk at Kee Tov!"

"Kee Tov, Michael?" Gramps looked at him questioningly. "You mean *Kee Ra*—not 'God saw that it was good' but 'God saw that it was bad'! One person hating another, one bad deed after another. Is that what you want this camp to be, Kee Ra?"

Michael didn't answer. Instead, he glared at Paul. Suddenly, he saw that Paul wasn't glaring back at him. To his surprise, Michael heard Paul pleading, "I'm sorry, Michael. I've had my lesson—don't think I haven't."

Michael stared. This was a sudden switch!

Paul told Michael everything just as he had told it to Gramps. He kept blaming himself, repeating over and over again that he didn't deserve being rescued by Gramps.

"Do you know what slander is, Paul?" asked Gramps after a while.

"I'm not sure."

"When you tell evil tales about your fellow man behind his back, it's called slander. You slandered when you told lies about Michael and Jeff. In allowing your anger to make you do cruel things, you hurt yourself. You hurt Michael when you forced your bunkmates to want to harm him. And you hurt your bunkmates when you made them believe something that wasn't true." Gramps stopped to look at Paul. "That's pretty serious, don't you think?"

Paul nodded his head. "I don't know why I did those mean things, Gramps. I guess I was so mad I couldn't think straight. I knew it was wrong." Paul squirmed unhappily, digging his heel into the earth. He lifted his face to Gramps. "Why did I do all those horrible things, Gramps?"

Paul's need for understanding and help reached into Gramps' heart.

"Within us are two selves," said Gramps, choosing his words carefully. "Our Rabbis explained it for us in the Talmud. The first self does good deeds and the second self does thoughtless deeds. Our better self tries to make us kind and considerate, honest and helpful. The other self makes us act in unkind and dishonest ways. We all must live with the two selves fighting to control us. In your case, Paul, the worse self won." Gramps paused to take a deep breath. "Now, are you going to let your worse self get away with that? It's up to you, and you alone, to decide."

Michael watched the flush spread over Paul's face. For the first time, Michael felt sorry for him. How was he going to face his bunkmates when he told them the truth? The thought of Paul's bunk believing the worst about him still burned in Michael's chest. He looked lovingly at Gramps. If only he could be as forgiving as Gramps. Everything changed when Gramps explained things.

"And Michael," added Gramps, "your better self has to decide what you will do, too. Your worse self is saying right now, 'Don't forgive Paul!' Are you going to let that self get away with it?"

Michael's eyes rested on Paul. It was a hard decision to make and no one could help him. All he had to do was hold out his hand. But something inside wouldn't let him. It's my worse self, he thought, understanding exactly what Gramps meant.

"Do you think I ought to tell Aaron?" asked Paul, his eyes clouding at the thought of confessing to Aaron.

"I'm not going to tell him, and I don't think Michael will tell him," answered Gramps.

"I guess I'd better tell him right away."

"How about your bunkmates? You have to clear Michael of those lies you told them."

Paul's sagging shoulders straightened. "I'll do it, Gramps!" He looked gratefully at the old man. Why hadn't he gone to him in the first place? Gramps always made a fellow see straight.

Michael gazed with new sympathy at Paul, glad he wasn't

in Paul's shoes. And right then, out came Michael's hand, straight into Paul's. Not a word was spoken. A shadow of a smile passed between them. They walked to the Big House, silently, with Gramps in the middle.

In the Big House Paul fidgeted under Aaron's steely eyes. Aaron had sent for his bunkmates right away. Paul felt their eyes on him as he faced the music. "You'll have to be punished, all of you," announced Aaron, looking around at the group with disappointment.

"But we told Jeff and Michael we were sorry and they said they'd forgive us. We won't do it any more," Seth pleaded for the group.

Paul's face was pale. He hadn't realized his bunkmates would have to be punished, too. Why should they suffer for his mistakes? He squared his shoulders. "It's not their fault. I talked them into it!"

"They knew it was wrong to gang up on Michael without giving him a chance to defend himself." Aaron hesitated before announcing the punishment. "None of you can go to campfire tonight!" With these words, Aaron opened the door and dismissed them. There was nothing more to say. The verdict was final!

Michael felt terrible about the punishment. "Jiminy!" he said to the boys, "I'd hate to feel that all of you had to suffer because I did something wrong." Michael bit his lip. "I think Paul's sorrier his bunkmates can't go to the campfire than he is because he can't go."

"Do you think it'll help if we ask Aaron to change his mind?" asked Joshua.

Michael brightened. "Let's get Paul and see. It's still an hour before the campfire."

When Paul heard what Emes planned to do for him, he shook his head hopelessly. "Aaron won't—and I don't blame him. I've been pretty dumb. The boys are sitting around the bunk as if the world was coming to an end. If only Aaron would let them go—I wouldn't feel like such a heel."

"Let's try," urged Michael.

On the way, Paul said, "I'd be willing to take three punishments if only Aaron would let the boys go to the campfire."

They faced Aaron again. First Michael talked—then Paul—and then the other boys.

Aaron listened quietly, not moving a muscle.

"All right, Paul," he said at last. "What are the three punishments you're willing to take so your friends can go to the campfire?"

"I'll wash the floor in your office," said Paul, looking at the length of the room. It was at least a mile long!

"Punishment number one!" said Aaron, holding up one finger.

"I'll peel potatoes for Joe tomorrow!" said Paul, thinking of the mountains of potatoes eaten at Kee Tov each day.

"Punishment number two!" Aaron held up two fingers. "One more!"

Paul's eyes wandered to the ceiling. He was stuck. Turning to Michael, he appealed to him for help, but Michael was at a loss, too. Nobody could think of another terrible punishment.

Jumping up from his chair, Aaron snapped his fingers. "I have it!" he cried. "You give Lovon your desserts for a week!"

The boys gulped. Paul's gulp was the loudest. Give his desserts away! That was about the worst thing that could happen to a growing boy. He swallowed hard. But, with a deep sigh, he said, "My desserts go to Lovon." And then a strange thing happened. As soon as he gave his desserts away, a wonderful feeling of peace came over him. For the first time that day he felt happy.

Just before the campfire, Aaron and Gramps appeared with Paul between them. The Y'lodim knew without being told that Gramps was responsible for Aaron's change of heart.

Gramps sat next to Michael. Silently, they watched the fire shoot flaming tongues into the dark sky.

Turning to Michael, Gramps said in a low voice, "The Rabbis in the Talmud asked, 'Who is the bravest hero?' And their answer was, 'He who turns an enemy into a friend.' "

Michael smiled into Gramps' eyes. "With your help, Gramps," he added.

WHAT DO YOU THINK?

1. A legend in the Midrash tells us that Joseph's brothers threw him into a pit swarming with snakes and scorpions. Simon, one of the brothers, was even more cruel than the others. He flung rocks at Joseph's head. But Joseph forgave him completely with his whole heart. When Simon was held as a hostage at Joseph's palace in Egypt while the other brothers went home to get Benjamin, Joseph saw that Simon had every comfort and the best of food.

   Does this legend prove the Talmud quotation, "It is merciful to help an enemy even if he doesn't deserve it"?

   How did Michael show that he didn't bear a grudge?

   What did Gramps say to Michael at the campfire that says the same thing?

   Do you think the title of the chapter, "Who Is the Bravest Hero?" is a good title? Why? Why not?

   Does changing an enemy into a friend help to "love peace and pursue it"? How?

   Have you ever had an experience where you turned an enemy into a friend with a kind deed? How did you feel?

2. Gramps told the campers this story from the Talmud at the campfire that night:

   A rabbi asked his servant, Tobi, to buy the very best food he could find at the market-place. Tobi re-

turned with a tongue. The next day the rabbi asked Tobi to buy the very worst food he could find. Again Tobi returned with a tongue.

"Why have you brought a tongue both times?" asked the puzzled rabbi.

Tobi smiled. "Because, dear Rabbi," he explained, "there is nothing better than a good tongue and there is nothing worse than a bad one."

"You are truly a wise man, Tobi," said the rabbi.

Why did Gramps tell this story?

How is this story like the quotation from Psalm 34 in the Bible that says, "Keep your tongue from speaking evil"?

3. In the Talmud the Rabbis tell us, "The slanderer hurts three: the slanderer himself, the one who is slandered, and the one to whom the slander is told."

How did Paul slander himself? How did he slander Michael? How did he slander his bunkmates? Did Saul have good reasons when he said he wouldn't go along with Paul's plans? Why? Why not? Was he trying to help Michael? How did Paul's bunkmates forget the law of justice that says, "In justice shall you judge your fellow man"?

Have you ever had an experience where you were called "chicken" because you failed to fall in with your gang's ideas when you thought they were wrong? What did you do? When you did what your conscience told you to do, how did you feel? Did anyone help you to face the problem or were you able to solve it yourself?

Can you remember a time when someone told a lie about you because he held a grudge? What did you do? Did you change the slanderer's attitude in any way? Did you become friends with him after a while? How did this experience follow the Bible commandment, "You shall not take revenge nor bear a grudge against the children of your people, but you shall love your neighbor as yourself"?

How did Paul's grudge against Michael and Jeff break this commandment?

4. Gramps explained to Paul about the good self and the bad self. The Talmud calls the good self, *yetzer ha-tov,* and calls the bad self *yetzer horo.*

Can you think of a time when you allowed your yetzer horo to win against your yetzer ha-tov? Can you think of a time when it happened the other way around, the yetzer ha-tov winning over the yetzer horo? Did anyone help you?

When did Paul's yetzer ha-tov begin to win? List all the things he did that prove your answer.

When did Michael's yetzer ha-tov begin to work?

When did Seth's yetzer ha-tov begin to win?

5. Bill also told this legend to the campers at the campfire. It comes from the Midrash.

One day, the king of Persia lay deathly ill. Nothing could cure him, said the doctor, except the milk of a mother lion. The king sent the doctor to the court of King Solomon for help. King Solomon instructed his most faithful servant to get the milk, and he told him how to do it. The servant gave fresh meat each day to a lioness in the royal zoo until she recognized him as her friend. Finally she allowed the servant to milk her.

The doctor hurried back with the precious milk. On the way one night he had a strange dream. All the parts of his body began to quarrel bitterly—his hands, feet, eyes, nose, ears, and his tongue. Each part claimed that it was responsible for saving the king's life.

When the tongue claimed that it was the most responsible, the other organs attacked the tongue and gave it a severe beating. "We shall see who is the most responsible," warned the tongue.

When the doctor arrived at the palace, the first question the king asked was, "Did you get the milk from the lioness for me?"

To his great surprise the doctor heard himself saying, "No, your majesty, I have brought the milk from a mother dog instead."

The angry king sentenced the man to be hanged. Just before the hanging, the tongue said to the other parts of the body, "See, I was right! It was I who told the king the lie. And only I can help the good doctor. If you do not admit right away that I am supreme, all of you will die." The frightened parts agreed readily that the tongue was right.

The doctor begged the king to grant him one last request. "Please drink of the milk I have brought." The king drank it and in an instant he was cured. The doctor was saved.

Is this story like the one Gramps told? How?

What can Paul learn from this story? His bunkmates?

What can you learn from this story?

6. Another Talmud story tells about a wealthy father with three sons.

The oldest son was very clever, the second son talked too much, and the youngest son never spoke at all. His brothers thought the youngest one was a fool but he really wasn't. He had a special rule for himself. Before he spoke he always warned himself, "Think three times before you speak."

One day, their father said to them, "God has been good to me and given me much wealth. When I am gone I wish to give my riches to the son who proves best that he can take care of himself in a strange city."

The three sons went to the city of Callah. Now the law of the city was that no man could live there unless he could answer a special riddle. To the oldest son, the wise man said, "With what can we close the mouths of our enemies when they slander us with lies?"

"With a blow of hard fists," he said quickly, "until they respect you with fear."

To the same riddle the second son replied, "To the fists, add severe tongue lashings."

The third son didn't know the answer. But he put into action his habit of thinking three times before he answered. He was silent for a long time. Much to his surprise the wise men were delighted. One said, "Without a word, this wise fellow has given us the proper answer. Silence alone can quiet slander."

What did the wise man mean by his last sentence?

How does this tie in with the advice in the Talmud that says, "Your friend has a friend, and your friend's friend has a friend, so be careful of what you say"?

If a person speaks badly about your friend, do you usually believe it? Do you try to find out if it is true before you judge the friend about whom you have heard the bad report?

7. The Bible also says, "It is your duty to warn someone who is doing a great wrong or you have a share in his sin."

What does this mean to you?

How did Paul's bunkmates break this commandment?

How did Michael and Jeff follow this commandment?

Have you ever had an experience where you wanted to warn a friend who was doing wrong? Were you afraid? Did you think it was none of your affair? What did you do?

Can you think of a time when you were grateful to someone for warning you in time when you were doing something wrong? Did the warning help to clear your thinking and change your action?

How can obeying the above commandment say, "Love your neighbor as yourself"?

How can it say Emes B'libo?

How can it say Kee Tov?

What does the Talmud rule, "All Israel are responsible for each other" mean to you?

Would you have allowed Paul and his bunkmates to attend the campfire if you had been Aaron? Why? Why not?

Why do you think Aaron changed his mind?

Did you like Paul better at the end of the chapter than you did at the beginning? Why?

How did Michael show Paul he had forgiven him?

Would you have forgiven Paul as Michael did? Why?

Have you ever had an experience where you were angry at a friend who harmed you, and after a while, you forgave him? What made you forgive him? Did you find it hard to do? How did it make you feel when you finally made friends again?

8. On Michael's street there are five boys who play together. Most of the time they get along very well. But one day Jimmy had a big fight with Peter because Peter squirted water on him and pushed him into a mud puddle. Jimmy gave Peter a bloody nose in return. As a punishment Jimmy's mother made him stay in the house all day Saturday. Peter's mother was upset, too, because Jimmy had given her son a bloody nose. She was the one who told his mother.

Jimmy waited for his chance to get even. It came one day while they were playing baseball in the Little League.

Jimmy was sure he saw Peter drop a very low flyball when he reached down to get it. But when the umpire called the runner "out," Peter said nothing. He wasn't sure whether the ball had touched the ground or not. But as long as the umpire said he had made the catch, Peter didn't argue.

Jimmy told the other boys that Peter had cheated. He wanted to throw Peter out of the gang because he hadn't told the truth. "No one," he said, "wants a cheat in his gang."

Let's dramatize this scene.

One person can be picked to take the part of a boy who tries to keep Peter from finding out he is being slandered.

Another can be the boy who thinks Jimmy is making a big fuss about nothing.

Another can be the one who doesn't want to break up the gang no matter what happens.

And another can be the boy who thinks Jimmy is wrong. He thinks Jimmy ought to stop talking about Peter behind his back unless he has definite proof that Peter really did cheat.

Write your own ending to this story.

9. On the last night of camp, Kee Tov had a wonderful banquet. When the campers entered the mess hall, the gleaming silver Tree of Life greeted them with outstretched arms. The menu matched the Torahs hanging from the Tree of Life. Here is the menu the children read:

MENU

TREE OF LIFE BANQUET

LOVINGKINDNESS FRUIT CUP
CONTENTED CHICKEN SOUP
KEE TOV SALAD
FORGIVE YOU TURKEY WITH GRATITUDE GRAVY
EMES B'LIBO STUFFING
CRANBERRIES IN COURAGE
MERCY POTATOES
HUMBLE LEMON CHIFFON PIE
HOSPITALITY PUNCH
ORANGE SHERBERT TOPPED WITH JUSTICE
TS'DOKO RELISH TRAY
PEACEFUL MINTS

Look back at the preceding chapters and find a mitzvah from the Bible or the Talmud that can match each food on the menu.

17. IT'S HARD TO BE GOOD

The twins had been home from Kee Tov for a week. One morning, Michael asked Marsha to help him with his baseball pitching. He didn't want to forget what Matt Johnson had taught him.

They practiced in the driveway. Marsha threw the ball at Michael. It rolled on the grass.

"You throw just like a girl," said Michael, scooping up the ball with both hands.

Marsha asked scornfully, "How else would I throw a ball, silly?"

"Like this, see!" With a big grin, Michael pumped his arm like a windmill and spun the ball into the air. But instead of zooming toward Marsha, the ball curved to the right, directly toward the side window of the house next door. Michael's grin vanished.

With an ear-splitting crash, the ball shattered the window! Aghast, the twins watched the glass fly in all directions.

The pulse in Marsha's throat jumped up and down like a grasshopper. "What'll we do?" she asked, her voice trembling.

"Let's get out of here—pronto," said Michael, his face pale. "We're really in a jam now." The only thing Michael could think of was the warning his parents had issued over and over again: *Do not play baseball near the house.*

They whizzed into the house like a cyclone. At the dining-room window the twins paused, out of breath, and peeked out into the deserted driveway. The jagged hole in the next-door window greeted them with a wicked eye.

Michael and Marsha knew that Mr. and Mrs. Pollen, their neighbors, had moved into the house during the summer. The Pollens went to their hardware store every morning and didn't return until early evening. Mother and Daddy had met them just once when they had first moved into the house.

"Well, anyway," said Michael, "nobody saw us do it."

"*Us?*" asked Marsha, surprised. "You mean *you*, don't you?"

"*You* helped. *You're* in this mess as much as I am."

"Oh, no, *I'm* not! You made me practice with you. If you hadn't been showing off, you wouldn't have thrown that crazy ball."

Michael knew his sister was right, but he scowled darkly at her, as if she were to blame for the accident. "Are you going to snitch on me?" he asked, point blank.

Marsha stared at him. "Why should I tell on you? You have to tell on yourself."

Michael tried to reason with her. "Look, nobody saw, and if we don't say anything, no one will find out."

"But you *have* to own up to it! Besides, they always find out. You know that!"

Michael could tell that Marsha was growing fearful. "Don't act so scared. If you act scared, Mother will smell it a mile away." Michael jutted out his lower lip, making himself look even more stubborn than he felt.

Marsha was about to reply when Mother came driving up the driveway. "Twins," she called, "please help me unload the bundles."

They rushed to help. In the kitchen Marsha waited for Michael to describe the accident, but he acted very busy storing away the groceries. She poked him on the shoulder, whispering, "Tell Mother, please, Michael!" But he shrugged her away without a word. His tongue seemed to be glued to the roof of his mouth.

The telephone rang and Michael ran to answer. Marsha heard him say, "Be right over." He banged down the receiver and ran out, shouting to his mother, "Jimmy wants me to help build a new model airplane. Be back for lunch."

Marsha walked over to the window. The hole seemed even larger now. "Why did Michael keep quiet?" she whispered to herself. "He knows he's wrong." She looked toward the kitchen where her mother was pouring gelatin into molds. How she wished she could tell Mother about it. But Michael would never speak to her again. He had to face up to what he did. She knew he would after he thought about it for a little while. Maybe he'd tell Mother at lunch.

Gramps flashed into Marsha's thoughts. She could hear his kind voice saying, "All of us are responsible for each other." She certainly felt responsible for her twin. But her lips were sealed, no matter what happened.

She looked at the hole again. If only the pieces of glass could magically jump back into place and make the window whole again! But that was the trouble with doing wrong things. Once you did them, they stayed done!

Michael didn't come home for lunch. He called to tell Mother that Jimmy's father had tickets for the ball game and had invited him along. Could he go? Mother told him to have fun.

"How can he even want to look at another baseball?" Marsha asked herself.

As Marsha ate lunch, she had no appetite. The salad tasted like cotton batting. The problem refused to leave her. "He'll tell when he comes home from the game," she kept thinking to herself. "He has to!" Had he forgotten Kee Tov and all Gramps' stories? Had he forgotten everything about how God wants us to act? God wouldn't want Michael to run away when he did something wrong. Somehow, Marsha had to help him remember what he was forgetting.

Pushing her half-finished plate away, Marsha gazed once more toward the broken window. Her heart felt heavier than three cheeses. What would the Pollens say when they discovered the damage? The twins hadn't even met them yet, and here they had broken their window. Michael wasn't being fair to them, either. She shook her head helplessly as each problem rose up like an ugly dragon.

Mother noticed that Marsha hadn't finished her lunch. Her usual sparkle was gone. "Aren't you feeling well, dear?" Mother asked.

"I have a headache," said Marsha, rubbing her hand across her brow.

Mrs. Ross felt Marsha's forehead. "I'd better take your temperature." But Marsha's temperature was normal. Just the same, Mother made her lie down and finally she fell asleep.

When Michael came home he met Daddy at the door. Marsha, her headache gone, tried to catch Michael alone, but he avoided her. He followed Daddy around the house describing each play in detail.

When Daddy decided to wash the car before supper, Michael insisted on helping. "Here, Daddy, let me do it," he said, taking the cleaning spray out of his father's hand. "I'll shine those windows sparkling clean."

Daddy was surprised. Usually he had to beg Michael to help with the car. Camp had certainly helped Michael, no doubt about that! "Thank you, Kee Tov!" chuckled Mr. Ross, gazing in the general direction of Sinai, New Hampshire.

Later, Michael insisted on helping Mother in the kitchen. "Here Mother," he said, taking the silverware from her hand, "let me set the table." Mother was just as astonished as

Daddy. Michael usually thought setting the table was girls' work. What she didn't know was what Michael kept telling himself, "When they punish me, they'll remember how hard I worked today, and they'll make the punishment easier." Without realizing it, he placed the forks in the spots where the knives and spoons belonged. His guilt hung over him like a sharp sword.

When Mother told him to wash before supper, Michael washed all the way up to his elbows instead of only to his wrists, the way he usually did. He helped Mother into her chair. But when he tried to help Marsha, she stepped on his toe hard. He could play-act and fool his parents but he couldn't fool her with his goodie-goodie ways!

Marsha gasped when he refused a second helping of chocolate cake, asking, "Are you sure there'll be enough for everybody?"

After supper, he brought over Daddy's pipe and slippers as Daddy was reading the evening paper. Daddy was beginning to feel uncomfortable. "Are you going to brush my teeth for me, too?" he laughed.

Michael didn't laugh at Daddy's joke. "When I don't do what you ask right away on the second, you get mad at me. And when I do things without being asked you still don't like it." Michael looked with disappointment at his father. "What does a fellow have to do to please his family?"

Instantly sorry, Daddy patted Michael on the back. "I apologize," he said. "It's just that we're not used to all this sudden service."

"You'd better get used to me this way," said Michael. "I'm a reformed character since Kee Tov." Michael looked around at his family, daring them to disagree. Marsha snorted.

It wasn't until Michael went out to empty the garbage pail that Marsha saw her chance. "You have to tell them *now!*" she insisted, grabbing his shirt sleeve. "Then they'll be able to tell Mr and Mrs. Pollen it was an accident."

Michael shrugged himself away. "Look how hard I'm work-ing," he said to her, "that ought to make up for some of it." At that moment, Michael was sure he could erase his earlier mis-take by being good now. He knew his sister wouldn't sell him down the river, no matter what happened. His eyes pleaded for her to understand. "Don't be such a worrier," he added, open-ing the back door.

Marsha tugged at his shirt and tried again. "God saw you break that window, Michael Ross! You know what Gramps said about running away from your problems. God is every-where watching! You've got to face it and tell!"

Michael swallowed the lump in his throat. Marsha was upset all right. Well, he was, too. "O.K. I'll tell them tomorrow. I can't today." He couldn't bear to alter the pleased expression on his parents' faces because he had been so helpful. Not just yet!

"But it'll be worse tomorrow," said Marsha, wisely. "You're letting your bad self win!"

"Tomorrow," promised Michael, walking inside.

In the living-room he glued his eyes to the television pro-gram, trying to shut out all the sights and sounds. The doorbell rang and Daddy went to answer it. Marsha blinked when she saw who was there. This was it! Mr. and Mrs. Pollen were standing at the door. Daddy invited them in and Marsha ran to tell Michael.

Michael felt his heart sink to his toes. Slowly he rose. The twins stood at the door with their faces as long as a train. They really looked worried.

Mr. Pollen came right to the point. "I wonder if you know anything about our broken window?" He held out a baseball. "We found this on our floor."

Mrs. Pollen added, "I don't know what we're going to do. We can't keep watch on the boys around here and at the same time be at the store." She looked at Mrs. Ross and asked, "Did you hear the sound of breaking glass today?"

"Why no, I didn't," said Mrs. Ross. She turned to the twins, "Did you?"

Michael could feel his knees buckling under him. Marsha felt cold prickles racing up and down her spine.

"No," came Michael's quick reply, "I was away all day."

Marsha gulped hard at Michael's lie. Before she could stop herself, she heard herself saying, "No," too.

"I guess I'll have to call the police," said Mr. Pollen. "Perhaps they can look into it." Daddy and Mother talked with the Pollens for a little while longer, and then the neighbors left.

Mrs. Ross shook her head in disgust when the visitors left. "What a mean thing to do," she said to Daddy. "I hope it wasn't anyone we know." It didn't occur to her that the twins could be responsible. She knew that Michael had been away all day and that Marsha had been inside with her. Why hadn't she heard the shattering of the glass? She hadn't stirred from the house all day. Mother had forgotten completely the half-hour she'd spent shopping that morning.

Michael felt like a criminal about to be led away to jail. What if the police questioned him? Would he be able to face them? Things were going from bad to worse. The lies he had told burned inside him. He looked at Marsha for help but she twisted her face away. Michael had made her lie, too. Tossing her head at him she flounced out of the room.

Michael followed his sister's exit through blurred eyes. Why hadn't he listened to Marsha? Digging his heel into the rug, he tried to gather up the courage he needed. But all that came out of his mouth was, "I'm going to bed."

His parents stared. Michael offering to go to bed without being asked! It was hard to believe!

"Are you sick?" they asked, together.

And then it came out of him in a whisper.

"I broke the window. I'm sorry." Michael hung his head, not daring to meet the looks he knew he would find in his parents' eyes.

Mr. and Mrs. Ross were speechless.

Michael lifted his eyes. The dark cloud on his father's face made him shiver. Dad's going to blow his top, he thought. Instead, his mother cried out, "Michael Ross! How could you stand there and tell the Pollens you knew nothing about that window? I'm ashamed of you!"

"I was afraid," said Michael, blinking his eyes.

Daddy said nothing. His eyes bored straight through Michael, making a hole bigger than the broken window.

"Was Marsha with you when it happened?" asked Mother, suddenly awakening to Marsha's odd behavior all afternoon. Before Michael could reply, she called, "Marsha, come here! We want to talk to you."

As soon as Marsha came into the room she knew that Michael had confessed. Six tons of bricks slid off her shoulders.

Michael began from the beginning and told his parents everything.

Daddy finally found his voice. "I'm surprised at you, Marsha. You knew Michael was wrong. It was your duty to tell us."

"But I've a duty to Michael, too. He's my brother and I like him. Please, Daddy, I'm sorry I told a lie. I didn't want to do it!" Salty tears stung her eyelids.

Michael rushed to his sister's defense. "Marsha begged me to tell you, but I wouldn't listen. She really tried, Dad!" Michael squirmed unhappily. "What are you going to do to me?" he asked, wanting to get the punishment over and done with.

"I'm not going to do anything, Michael. You're going to do it. You just march over to the Pollen house and tell them what you did."

Michael's feet stuck to the floor. "I'm afraid."

"March!" said Daddy, quietly but firmly.

Marsha's heart flip-flopped. "I'll go with you, Michael," she offered.

"No, you don't, Marsha. He has to face the Pollens all by himself," said Daddy. "And Michael, you will now have to pay for the window from your allowance. You know that, don't you?"

Michael nodded. He watched his allowance say good-bye for at least a year and a half. This time the carpet had certainly been yanked from under his feet.

Marsha insisted on going with Michael. "I'm to blame, too. Didn't I tell a lie? I have to tell Mr. and Mrs. Pollen I'm sorry."

Mother agreed.

Outside, the twins walked slowly as if they were going to meet their doom. As they reached the Pollen house, they turned to look back. Framed in the window were their parents, watching them.

With a shaking finger Michael pressed the doorbell.

"Come in, Twins," said Mrs. Pollen, when she saw them. Near the telephone Mr. Pollen was deep in conversation. "He's calling the police," Michael whispered to his sister. His throat swelled with fear. Was it too late?

Mr. Pollen finished and he joined his wife and the twins. Without losing another second, Michael began. "I—I—I—I came to tell you I broke your window. I'm sorry. I was afraid to admit it before."

"I helped him," added Marsha, rushing to share part of the blame. "Did you call the police?"

"Not yet," said Mr. Pollen with a serious face.

"I'll pay for the window," said Michael, quickly. "How much is it going to cost?"

"I'll have to check with the repair man. I'll tell you when I find out."

Marsha looked through the door to the dining-room. She could hear the wind swishing through the broken window. The glass was scattered all over the rug. "Please let me help pick up the glass?" she begged Mrs. Pollen.

"Thank you, no, Marsha. It won't be safe. I'll use the

vacuum later." When Mrs. Pollen saw Marsha's disappointment, she added, "Don't worry, dear."

"I bet you think I'm the meanest kid on the street," said Michael, looking first at Mr. Pollen and then at his wife.

For the first time the Pollens smiled. "Not at all, Michael," laughed Mr. Pollen. "My children are married now, but when they were your age they used to get into trouble just like you. And Michael, I'm going to let you in on a little secret, I've broken some windows in my day, too."

Michael began to feel better. "You did!" he exclaimed.

"I certainly did! We all have our detours. The important thing is that you were man enough to admit it and face up to it—head on."

"But I didn't admit it right away," said Michael, still ashamed of the way he had acted all day.

"That's true. It's a hard thing to learn. But as long as you finally did the right thing, you're still ahead of the game."

"Gosh, you're swell!" cried Michael, feeling as if he had been given another chance. "I'm glad you're our neighbor."

They stayed for an hour after that. The twins were telling Mr. and Mrs. Pollen about Kee Tov and the wonderful fun they had had. Before they left, Mr. Pollen said, "Just one thing more, Michael. Do you think you can move your baseball field to an open spot?" He twinkled at Michael and ended up with, "Far away from my windows!"

Outside, Michael was thoughtful. "You know, Marsha, here we are, home one week from Kee Tov and look at all the trouble I caused today."

Marsha nodded. "I know. But it's hard to be good. Do you remember what Gramps said the night of the banquet?"

Their memories swept them back to Kee Tov.

Aaron had removed the golden Torahs from the silver Tree of Life and had given them to the bunks that had earned them. The campers fitted the Torahs into grooves carved into little

wooden boats, so that each Torah formed a sail. In front of each Torah sail was a small opening in which they placed a single candle. Soon a long parade formed and marched to the lake front, all holding the Torah boats aloft and singing happily. Counselors with flaming torches lighted the path.

At the shore they faced a round silvery moon, riding low in the sky. It shone on the lake below changing the water to hammered silver. The counselors helped the children light their candles. Just before they set their boats adrift, Gramps said, "These Torah boats tell us a wonderful story. They tell us that you have tried to obey God's commandments all summer. As these Torah boats sail away, we hope that you will obey these good laws not only at camp, but wherever you go. Not just some of the time, but *all* the time."

The moon came to rest just above Gramps' head and suddenly his face was flooded with silver. "It's hard to be good," he said, smiling at the listening children. "Being good isn't something you can learn in one summer. It takes a whole lifetime, and you have just begun."

The campers stood motionless as they watched the golden fleet skim and dip over the water, the candlelights dancing in the moonlight. A light breeze caught the sails, tilting the boats to one side. Silence hung over the camp as one by one the candles flickered and vanished into the darkness.

"Gramps is right," said Marsha, pulling herself back to the present. "It's hard to be good."

"We have to keep working at it each day," agreed Michael, "and I'm going to begin right now."

Into the house they ran with glowing faces.

"I'm never going to be bad again," promised Michael.

"Me, too," promised Marsha.

Mother and Daddy knew that their twins would be the best children in the world—for a few days!

"Until the next time," they chuckled together.

Daddy added, "If you didn't do wrong things, we'd worry.

Just remember, we'll keep on loving you no matter what you do. We keep hoping you'll grow better each day."

"And God saw that it was good," said Mother with a loving smile.

"Kee Tov," said Michael and Marsha together, with shining eyes. "Kee Tov!"

WHAT DO YOU THINK?

1. Michael should have remembered this story Gramps told from the Chasidic Rabbis.

   One day a rabbi was traveling in a carriage from one Polish town to another. Suddenly the driver stopped the carriage near a field with new-mown hay piled into a high mound. "Watch carefully," said the driver to the rabbi, "if anyone comes, shout a warning to me."

   The driver gathered a heaping armful of hay and as he turned to put it into the carriage, the rabbi shouted a warning with thunder in his voice. Dropping the hay quickly, the driver leaped into his carriage and sped away from the spot. Looking back, he saw no one in the field. "Why did you lie to me, Rabbi?" he asked, angrily.

   "But I didn't lie to you, my son," said the rabbi, gently. "You were seen—you were seen by God who sees everything."

   How could Gramps' story help Michael?

   How can it help you?

2. At the final banquet, each camper received a copy of *Kolenu*, the Kee Tov magazine, to take home. Aaron told the campers that *Kolenu* meant "our voice," and he called attention to a poem written by one of the children. He said that it expressed what he hoped Kee Tov had helped the campers learn that summer.

   Etz Chayim
   O Tree of Life
   So wondrous fair,

You guide our days
With loving care.

Your roots reach far
To anchor deep
Our trust in God,
Our faith to keep.

Your trunk upright,
So sturdy, tall,
Gives strength to know
And hear God's call.

Your branches spread
Their crowns of shade,
Protecting us
When we're afraid.

Your fruit is ripe
With loving deed,
With justice, truth
And peace we need.

Your flowers bright
Make hearts aware
To know that God
Is everywhere.

Why did Aaron think this poem expressed best what he hoped Kee Tov had taught the children?

Look back to Chapter 2 to what Gramps told the campers on the first night, when they chose the new name for the camp. Does this poem say the same thing? In what way?

How was the silver Tree of Life hung with Torahs of service like the fifth stanza in this poem?

How does the poem show that the author finds God everywhere?

In Chapter 2 Gramps felt sure that the Torah would be safe in the hands of the campers. What do you think he meant?

Think of the children in Emes and S'goolo. Tell how each changed after the summer at Kee Tov.

Which boy would you like for your best friend? Why?

Which girl would you like for your best friend? Why?

Which adult would you like to help you if you had a serious problem?

Does knowing God's commandments make any difference in the way you act toward yourself, your family and your friends? Why?

3. Someone said that, "The center of the Jewish religion is commandment and deed."

   Do you agree with this? Why? Would you agree if this said, "The center of the Jewish religion is commandment"? Why? Why not? Would you agree if it said, "The center of Jewish religion is deed"? Why? Why not?

   Look back through the various chapters in the book.

   Which deed did you like the best? Why?

   Which deed did you like the least? Why?

   What deed reminds you of an experience that happened to you this year? Did it help you decide what to do? In what way?

4. One of the stories Gramps told the children in the Thinking Place came from the Midrash.

   King Solomon's greatest task was to build the holy Temple in Jerusalem. He spent many months searching for the right place on which to build a Temple dedicated to the service of God. It had to be the best place he could find. One night, he could not sleep because of his problem and decided to go for a walk. He found himself on Mt. Zion wandering through a barley field owned by two brothers. It was harvest time.

   One brother was unmarried and very poor. The other brother was blessed both with riches and many children.

   It was in this field just at midnight that King Solomon found the solution to his problem.

   Under cover of darkness the poor brother brought his ripe grain and added it to the store of his rich brother, thinking that his brother had many mouths

to feed and needed it more. The rich brother added his ripe grain to the store of the poor brother, thinking that he would not have enough to eat.

When King Solomon saw the great love and devotion between these two brothers he knew immediately that God would want His holy Temple built in this place. He bought the field from the brothers and hastened to build the Temple.

How was Marsha like the brothers in the story?

Has your brother or sister ever helped you to face a problem? How?

Have you ever been stubborn like Michael about admitting a mistake?

Have you ever worried about someone you loved who was making a mistake? What did you do?

Can you think of a time when you helped a friend face a problem? What happened?

How is the way you face your problems connected with "You shall love your neighbor as yourself"? With "Emes B'libo"? With "Kee Tov"?

5. In the Bible it tells us that after Cain murdered his brother, God asked him where Abel was. Cain answered, "I know not. Am I my brother's keeper?"
   Another word for keeper is "protector."

   What would be your answer to Cain? Why?

   What was Marsha's answer in the last chapter?

   Do you think this means that we must protect only our brothers?

   Does it apply to your neighbor, too? How?

   What quotation did Marsha think of in the story that means the same thing?

6. In the Bible we also have the story of Jonathan and David.
   Jonathan's father, King Saul, hated David because he thought David wanted to steal his throne. Jonathan loved his father and he loved David. When

King Saul tried to kill David, Jonathan was forced to make a hard choice.

Should he allow his father to kill David, his best friend, or should he warn David of his father's intention? And even when Jonathan was warned by his father that David would take the throne that rightfully belonged to the son of King Saul, Jonathan saved David's life. Nothing could stand in the way of their great friendship.

How was Marsha like Jonathan?

Can you remember a time when you did something wrong to help a friend? What made you do it? How did it make you feel?

Do you think Michael was right when he did all the good deeds around the house so that his punishment would be less severe? Why? Why not?

Have you ever done this, too? What happened?

Have you a best friend? Why have you chosen this person as your best friend?

7. This Midrash was in *Kolenu*, the camp magazine. Marsha read it to her mother when she came home from Kee Tov.

A rich man wanted to make his slave happy. He gave him his freedom and a shipload of valuable goods, saying, "Sail to various countries and sell these goods. Whatever you receive shall be yours to keep."

On the voyage there arose a raging storm. The ship was wrecked but the slave managed to swim safely to an island. He wandered about the strange island and suddenly came to a magnificent city. Many people came to welcome him, hailing the amazed slave as their king. They brought him to a splendid palace, and dressed him in royal robes and a golden crown. When the slave asked why the people were honoring a poor shipwrecked man in this way, a wise man stepped forward and replied, "On our island we pray each year that a man will be sent to be our king. You have been sent to answer our prayer. For one year you will be our king with all the power a king should have. At the end of the year, your crown will be taken away, and you will lose your power. You will be taken

to a deserted island and there you will live the rest of your days. The kings who have come before you did not think of preparing for the future. Take heed, O King, and do not do as they did."

The new king listened well and decided that he did not want the same fate. "Advise me, O wise men," he asked, "how may I prepare for the future?"

"Send workmen to the island to which you will be banished. Bid them build new houses and cultivate farms. If there are houses in which to live and food to eat, the island will attract people who will wish to live there. When the time comes for you to travel there, they will be ready to welcome you and love you as their king."

The new king followed their advice. Instead of dreading the day when he would be banished, he now looked forward to the day when he would start his new life. When he finally came to the island, the people welcomed him with joy. And he lived among them as their king in peace and happiness.

Mother said, "This house is like the island the king built. We can make it good and beautiful by our good deeds."

Why did Mother say this to the twins?

When do you find it hardest to be good? Why?

When do you find it easiest to be bad? Why?

What did Mr. and Mrs. Pollen say that helped the twins?

What did Mr. and Mrs. Ross say that helped the twins?

How is forgiveness connected with working hard to be good?

What did Gramps mean when he ended his talk at the lake front with, "And you've just begun"?

What does it have to do with facing the truth about yourself—"Emes B'libo"?

What has it to do with "Love your neighbor as yourself"?

What has working each day at being good have to do with "Kee Tov"?